Building stones
of
England and Wales

Norman Davey

Published for the Standing Conference
for Local History by the BEDFORD SQUARE PRESS
of the National Council of Social Service

Published for the Standing Conference
for Local History by the Bedford Square Press
of the National Council of Social Service,
26 Bedford Square, London WC1

Distributed by Research Publications Services Ltd.,
Victoria Hall, East Greenwich, SE10 0RF

Typeset and printed in England by Lowe & Brydone, Thetford

Contents

Fig. 1 Distribution of the principal limestone quarries
(Those still operating are shown in black)

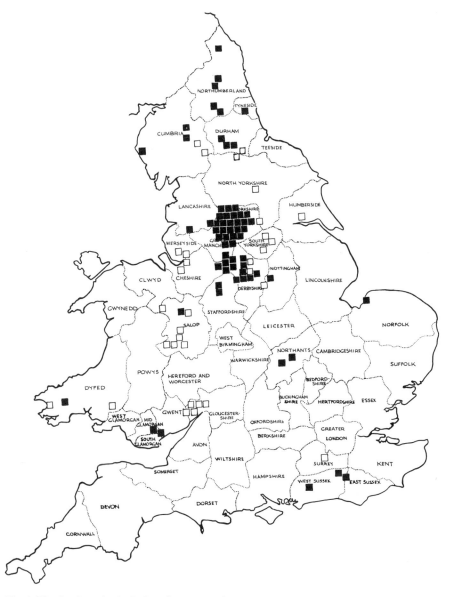

Fig. 2 Distribution of principal sandstone quarries.
(Those still operating are shown in black)

Fig. 3 Distribution of slate and grantie quarries.
   (Those still operating are shown in black. The slate quarries are shown as diamonds, the granite quarries as triangles)

Introduction

Stone is our most beautiful and enduring material for building and in England and Wales we are particularly fortunate in having abundant supplies of it. Many examples of its use have survived from prehistoric times. The stone circles at Avebury and Stonehenge in Wiltshire are but two which bear testimony to this. In a particular locality, and certainly in any particular quarry, the type and quality of the stone may vary greatly, and the selection of stone suitable for building must depend on a number of factors such as physical structure, whether, for example, the material is laminated or occurs in the quarry in homogeneous beds of sufficient thickness to provide blocks of reasonable thickness and size. The chemical composition is important; to know whether the stone will weather well, or will not interact detrimentally with other materials which come into contact with it. Limestone, for example, should not, as a general rule, be laid against sandstone for the two materials may interact chemically. The colour and texture of the stone may also influence its choice. Even in one quarry the colour of the beds of stone may vary, offering a wide range of choice to the architect. He may prefer one colour tone to another, to enhance the appearance of his building, and to harmonise with its surroundings.

Due to difficulties of transport long ago, stone was often limited to a large extent to local use. Therefore a study of early churches in a locality, or of other historic buildings such as monastic structures, castles and cathedrals, will often provide very valuable information on the type and durability of stone. It may also be possible to trace the location of the quarry whence the stone was obtained and to procure samples for reference. This in itself would form a most valuable study. People living in the area may be able to give information on local quarries, and a study of ancient building records preserved in county record offices and elsewhere may also lead to interesting results.

Many different kinds of rock have been used for building, but they fall broadly into two main groups, the primary, or igneous, rocks, such as granite, syenite, diorite, dolerite, and basalt, formed by cooling and solidification of a molten magma; and the secondary, or sedimentary, rocks such as limestones and sandstones, formed by the disintegration and decomposition of the primary rocks and the subsequent deposition and consolidation of the products in a stratified form.

There is a further group of rocks termed metamorphic. They are derived from pre-existing solid rock masses, either igneous or sedimentary, by the action of heat, pressure, or chemical fluids acting separately or together to form a distinctive new type of stone. For example, gneiss, which generally has the same composition as granite, is derived by crystallisation from igneous rocks; quartzite is similarly produced by crystallisation from sandstone; marble by metamorphism from limestone; and slate is derived from argillaceous sediments or fine-grained volcanic ashes by metamorphism.

Igneous Rocks

The igneous rocks are divided into three groups: Plutonic, Hypabyssal, and Volcanic. Those in the Plutonic group include granite, syenite, diorite and gabbro, and they occur in nature as major intrusions of material which solidified well below the earth's surface under conditions of slow cooling. They are completely crystalline and coarse grained. The Hypabyssal group, including quartz porphyry, syenite porphyry, and dolerite, occur naturally as minor intrusions of material which solidified below the earth's surface in small wall-like or sheet-like bodies known respectively as dykes or sills. They are either completely or almost completely crystalline and fine grained. Rocks of the Volcanic group include ryolite, obsidian, trachyte, andesite and basalt. They exist as surface extrusions of materials discharged at the surface of the earth, or on the seabed, and are incompletely crystalline and very finely grained or are non-crystalline (glassy). Associated with volcanic igneous rocks are a number of fragmental rocks which may almost be classed as sedimentary rocks. They include volcanic agglomerates or coarse tuffs, tuff and ashes and trass. Clearly igneous rocks form a complex group of materials not all suitable for building purposes. Although geologically granite is a closely defined type of rock, the name has been applied rather loosely to many other igneous rocks by the stone industry. The more important quarries for granite are situated in Cornwall and Devon, where the material is mostly muscovite (containing white mica) biotite (containing black mica) granite, and in Westmoreland and Wales where the material is mostly porphyritic granite.

Sedimentary Rocks

Of the sedimentary rocks, sandstones consist essentially of the more durable fragments of igneous rocks, such as quartz, felspar and mica cemented together by siliceous matter, calcium and magnesium carbonates, iron compounds, or clay. They are formed by the degradation of the igneous rocks by weathering processes, followed by the transportation of the weathered fragments by wind and water, and their deposition on land or in water where their partial or complete consolidation may occur by the introduction of cementing material in solution, and by subsequent pressure. Depending on the type of cementing material sandstones are classed as siliceous (like Darley Dale stone of the carboniferous system), calcareous, or dolomitic (like Red Mansfield stone of Permian system in Nottinghamshire), ferruginous, or argillaceous (clay cemented). Their texture varies from coarse to very fine, particularly in those samples which were formed from wind-blown deposits. Sili-

ceous sandstones, like those from Darley Dale and Stancliffe are very durable. Calcareous and dolomitic sandstones which, as their name implies, are cemented with calcium carbonate and magnesium carbonate respectively, are generally less durable than the siliceous type. Sometimes sandstones are classified according to their geological age rather than on a lithological basis; for example, Jurassic sandstone, Cretaceous sandstone, and Triassic sandstone, Permian sandstone, or Carboniferous sandstone, but the classification based on the type of cementing material is perhaps more useful when choosing stone for building construction.

Limestones consist essentially of calcium carbonate formed either by precipitation from sea water as small spheroidal (oolitic) calcareous grains, or by the accumulation of the shells and skeletons of marine organisms. The deposits are further cemented together by calcium carbonate in solution. Limestones can be grouped lithologically according to their composition and physical characteristics as follows. Shelly limestone (like Hopton Wood stone from Middleton, near Wirksworth, Derbyshire, of Carboniferous system) containing shells of marine organisms; crinoidal limestone, containing fragments of stems and 'arms' of crinoids, the so called 'sea lilies', foraminiferal limestone (like Beer stone from South Devon) containing microscopic marine animals in shells, known as foraminifera; coral limestone, containing skeletons of coral and calcareous algae, stromato poroids, and mollusca (of Devonian and Carboniferous system); bryozoa limestone (like the magnesian limestone of Yorkshire) containing bryozoa or mosslike animals; dolomitic and magnesian limestone (like the Carboniferous limestones of Derbyshire and South Wales), formed either by the alteration of normal limestone or chemically deposited rock (like Mansfield and Bolsover Moor stone of the Permian system); oolitic limestone, like Ketton stone, often called oolite, or roestone, composed mainly of small spherical bodies (oolites) consisting of concentric rings of calcium carbonate deposited around sand grains, or fragments of shell, or coral, and cemented together with crystalline calcite (calcium carbonate); tufa, known to the Greeks as *poros*; and travertine limestone, often porous, formed by the redeposition of calcium carbonate taken up in solution by water flowing through older calcareous rocks.

Geologically, tufa and travertine are the more recent of the limestones; and they occur in localised deposits, around springs.

As in the case of sandstones, limestones may also be classified according to their geological age, eg Permian limestone, Rhaetic and Triassic limestones, Carboniferous limestone and Devonian limestone. Some of the limestones are particularly hard, and can be highly polished to resemble marble.

Purbeck 'marble' from the Purbeck beds, near the top of the Upper Jurassic rock in the Isle of Purbeck, near Swanage has been used since Roman times and was a favourite material with English mediaeval architects, particularly for slender clustered columns and sepulchral monuments. It contains myriads of shells of the freshwater snail *Paludina carinifera,* embedded in a greenish, or bluish-grey limestone, It can be easily confused with some varieties of the Sussex marble, which occurs in thin beds in the Wealden clay, in the Petworth area, which is of Lower Cretaceous system. It contains shells of *Paludina,* but principally *P. sussexienis* and *P. fluviorum.* Examples of the use of Purbeck marble can be seen in the columns of Westminster Abbey, in part of the Shrine of Edward the Confessor, and in the cathedrals of Lincoln, Winchester, Worcester and Salisbury. Sussex marble was used for the altar stones and episcopal chair in Canterbury Cathedral.

Other 'marbles' or hard limestone, able to take a high polish have been obtained from various localities. At Ashburton, in Devon, a limestone of Devonian age has given a 'marble' dark grey to black in colour, with white and red patches and veins. Other colourful rocks with reddish tints have come from the Torquay and Newton Abbot area. The Petitor quarry at Torquay, for example has produced three varieties known as Petitor Grey and Pink, Petitor Grey (Petitor Spot) generally grey in colour but containing many fossils, and Petitor Pink, predominantly pink in colour with brown and red markings, with veins and patches of grey and yellow. From Ketley, near Yealmton, also in Devon has come a green 'marble', also of Devonian system.

In Somerset the best known 'marbles' are the grey and green ones of the Quantocks, the black 'marble' of Cheddar, and the brown 'marble' nearer Bristol. Farther north in Derbyshire are the carboniferous 'marbles' such as Hopton Wood, from Matlock, and Hadene Derbyshire Fossil, the former being a pleasant cream colour. In the past black limestone from Ashford and a mottled grey limestone from Monyash, also in Derbyshire, have been used as 'marbles'.

In Westmoreland a white 'marble' was quarried in the eighteenth century near Kendal. It was veined with red and other tints. Also near Ambleside was quarried a green coloured 'marble' veined with white, and an almost black one near Kirby Lonsdale.

Some types of limestone and sandstone, and calcareous sandstone are of a fissile nature and can be easily split into thin layers, from which roofing tiles can be formed. Sometimes the freshly dug slabs of stone, or 'pendles', were laid flat on the ground and left until the winter frosts commenced to split them horizontally. Sometimes they had to be left throughout the whole winter for this to happen and they had to be wetted in order to encourage splitting. A tile-maker completed the splitting by means of a special hammer with a sharp curved edge. Then he rested the pieces of stone upon a horizontal iron blade mounted in a heavy block, trimmed them to the required shape, and pierced a hole in them with a pick, at a suitable point near the top so that they could be hung to the roof battens by oak pegs or clouts.

The technique is very old. The Romans used many stone roofing tiles, some almost oval in shape, others four, five, or six-sided pointed or slightly rounded at their lower extremity. The Romans went to some trouble to obtain suitable materials. For example, for their villa at Chedworth, in Gloucestershire, they used not only the local limestone, but also sandstone from the Forest of Dean. The craft has continued in England and Wales since the Roman times, but on a much reduced scale.

Rocks suitable for tile making occur in the following geological strata:
(a) Cambrian and Silurian, with its highly micaceous sandstone of the Upper Silurian (Ludlow group) quarried to the north of Amman-ford in South Wales, and the slate stone, known as 'Green Slate' rock, quarried at Honister Crag, near Keswick.
(b) Devonian, producing the fissile sandstone of the Old Red Sandstone in South Wales.
(c) Carboniferous, producing thin flaggy sandstone, from Wales, Derbyshire, Lancashire and Yorkshire.
(d) Jurassic, rocks from the Lias formation in Somerset and Shropshire; from marl-stone in Wiltshire; from calcareous sandstone (Duston slate) from Duston in Northamptonshire; from the calcareous sandstone at the base of the Great Oolite at Stonesfield, between Charlbury and Woodstock in Oxfordshire, Eyford and Kyneton Thorns in Gloucestershire, and other parts of the Cotswold area; from thin limestone of the Forest Marble, which occurs in several small quarries in Gloucestershire; from hard siliceous limestone at Brandsby, Yorkshire, and from the Lower Purbeck beds in Dorset.
(e) Cretaceous, producing Horsham Stone of the Wealden beds in Sussex.

Metamorphic Rocks

A third group are the metamorphic rocks. These are formed from either igneous or sedimentary rocks which have been subjected to the effects of heat or pressure, or of both these combined. Their form has therefore been changed, igneous rocks into gneisses, clays into slates, sandstones into quartzites and limestones into marbles. The only rocks so formed and used in building are the slates and marbles. Although slate is extensively quarried in England and Wales, marbles are scarce. Most of the so-called marbles are limestones which are capable of receiving a high polish, for example, Purbeck marble and Sussex marble. They both contain fossils which of course, would have disappeared had the limestone undergone the re-crystallisation which occurs with true marbles.

Slate is a sedimentary argillaceous stone produced by metamorphism of primary or igneous rocks. The original material in the form of fine clay, sometimes with sand or volcanic dust, was deposited under water and consolidated by vertical pressure into mudstone and shale. In this condition the sedimentary particles were cemented by carbonates of lime and magnesia, by kaolin, or by various iron compounds. Intense heat and great lateral pressure subsequently converted the product into slate, the kaolin and felspar of the original sediment being transformed into sericite, a potash bearing mica which had a crystalline form of minute overlapping flakes and fibres in planes running at right angles to the direction of pressure. This structure imparted great strength and elasticity to the material. The cleavage planes formed in the material do not necessarily coincide with, and may in fact be quite oblique to, the sedimentation beds formed during the deposition of the original material.

Limestone Quarries

Of the stones for building, limestone is that most widely used. It occurs in a band stretching across England from East Devon and Dorset, to Lincolnshire and into Yorkshire (Figure 1). The stone varies in structure, texture and colour at different points along this ridge and the variations in quality are reflected in the character and appearance of the buildings in the towns and villages from south to north.

Limestone from Beer on the coast of Lyme Bay, near Seaton in East Devon, has been used locally for many years, particularly for churches, as for instance for the tower of Sidmouth Church dating from the fifteenth century. The stone was shipped to London where it was used in 1347 for the King's Chapel at Westminster, and shortly after for work at the Tower of London and later for some parts of Christopher Wren's cathedral of St Paul's. Transport by water was much easier and less costly than by road and trackway, and stones quarried along the coastline, as at Beer, and in river estuaries and valleys were often delivered to sites some hundred miles away. Beer stone was also used at Exeter Cathedral, being carried there directly by boat along the coast and up the River Exe.

Eastward along the coast are the very important quarries of Portland stone, situated for the most part on the Isle of Portland itself. The stone of the Jurassic Period is a shelly oolitic limestone, greyish-white, or cream in colour. The quarries are very extensive and deep, often 40 feet or more. The earliest workings were naturally on or near the cliff face, so that the stone could be loaded directly into boats. Some of the quays, built in the eighteenth century specially for loading stone still exist, as for example Forbes Pier and Kings Pier. The principal beds of the limestone, are the Whitbed, a fairly uniform and close grained stone, the Roach bed of shelly and rather coarse textured stone, often used for ashlar work, and the Basebed of more even textured stone, fine grained and comparatively free from shell. Beneath

13

the Basebed some attractive crystalline limestone, called Pericot, has been worked more recently and is suitable for slab walling.

Portland stone has been used for centuries. In the fourteenth century it was used, like Beer stone, at Exeter Cathedral, being transported by ship. It was in the seventeenth century after the Great Fire that it came into great prominence for rebuilding London. Sir Christopher Wren used it in the reconstruction of St Paul's Cathedral, and for the fifty or so towers and turrets of the City churches. He also used it for Greenwich Hospital. Other random examples of its use in London are Horse Guards, Somerset House, Bank of England, National Gallery and the Law Courts. Inigo Jones used it for the famous Banqueting House in Whitehall. A more recent and different use was for the new Waterloo Bridge, where the Portland stone was used in vertical courses, for facing the structure. The headquarters of the Royal Institute of British Architects in Portland Place, London and the Royal Air Force Pavilion at Brookwood Cemetery are two more examples worthy of note.

The Isle of Purbeck, also in Dorset, produces the famous so-called 'Purbeck marble'. It is a limestone of the Jurassic Period, consisting of a tough conglomerate of freshwater snail shells, varying in colour from light grey to dark grey, and to blue, and is capable of taking a high polish. The stone was used by the Romans and slabs of it have been found on some of their town sites as far away as Viroconium (Wroxeter) near Shrewsbury. It has also been used in church building since the late twelfth century particularly for slender detached shafts, foliated capitals, column bases, string courses

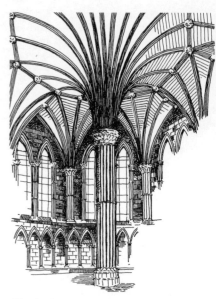

Fig. 4 Chapter House, Lincoln Cathedral.

and for flooring. Many examples of its use can be seen throughout the country. One is illustrated in Figure 4, which shows the clustered columns of Purbeck marble in the Chapter House at Lincoln Cathedral. This stone came from a quarry at Worth Matravers, whose quarries are still operating. Keates quarry and St Aldhem's quarry are two others. In fact quarries, and many old workings, abound in the South Hills from Swanage to Worth Matravers, and along the coast from Anvil Point to St Albans Head. Quarries are also still working at Langton Matravers, Herston, near Swanage, and at Swanage itself. There is hardly a church of the thirteenth and fourteenth century throughout England that does not contain some architectural details in Purbeck marble. Ely, Exeter, Norwich, Lincoln and Salisbury cathedrals are but a few examples, but

14

the great pillars of the nave at Westminster Abbey, built between 1387 and 1404 are notable. A local example of its use is in part of the Norman church of St Nicholas at Studland, not far from Swanage.

A considerable amount of limestone has in the past been quarried in the Isle of Wight. Much of it has been used in buildings on the island. For example, stone quarried at Binstead was used in the twelfth century for some neat squared masonry at Carisbrook Castle, and later during repairs Bonchurch stone was used there for some large quoins. Bembridge limestone was used for Yarmouth Castle, and it was from Yarmouth that much of the Isle of Wight stone was shipped into Hampshire and the Southern counties. Binstead stone, and some from Ventnor, was used for Arreton Manor, built about 1612, with an east wing dating from the fourteenth century. Shipped to the mainland, Binstead stone and Quarr stone were used for facing the Norman keep of Arundel Castle. Stone from Quarr was also used for Beaulieu Abbey founded by King John in 1204 for Cistercian or White monks. Stone from Bonchurch and Bembridge was used at Porchester Castle in 1397, and some from Selborne at Winchester Castle. When William of Wykeham carried out repairs to the nave of Winchester Cathedral he obtained stone from Binstead, and commissioned the Abbot of Quarr Abbey to transport it by sea. The Quarr quarries were particularly interesting for they were close to and owned by Quarr Abbey which was founded in 1132 by Baldwin de Redvers, Earl of Devon, for Benedictine monks.

Somerset produces several important grades of limestone. The mountain limestone of the Carboniferous series stretches from the west of Bristol along the Mendip Hills to the famous Cheddar Gorge, where the massive formation is most spectacular. Some of the stone is worked at the Battscombe quarry, near Cheddar. It is light grey to pink in colour. Limestone of the Jurassic Oolite series comes from Doulting near Shepton Mallet and is light brown in colour. The St Andrew quarry at Doulting supplied the stone for the façade of Wells Cathedral, and can be seen to great advantage there particularly on the west front. More recently Doulting stone has been used for the new government buildings in Whitehall, London, and for facing some of the bridges on the M2 and M5 motorways, at Warndon junction, near Worcester, for example. Another type of limestone is Ham Hill Stone from Ash near Martock, which has been worked since Roman times. A shelly limestone of the Jurassic Lias series, fawny brown in colour, it was used in the beginning of the fourteenth century for building the Priory at Stoke-sub-Handon in Somerset, now in the care of the National Trust, and later on for the beautiful Montacute House, also a National Trust property. This latter house was built by Sir Edward Philips between 1588 and 1601. At the church of St Mary the Virgin at Cerne Abbas, Ham Hill stone was used for the tower and front of the church and for the walls of the Lady Chapel. Similar lias limestone has been dug at Charlton Mackrol.

Limestone from the Dundry quarries to the south-west of Bristol was used for many of the buildings of mediaeval Bristol. St Mary Redcliffe is a particularly fine example of its use, and should be visited. Queen Elizabeth I in 1574 aptly described the church as the 'fairest, the goodliest and most famous church in England'. Stone similar to that from Dundry was quarried at Felton, Broadfield and elsewhere; and there are many disused quarries in the Mendip and Quantock Hills.

Perhaps the most famous Somerset stone is that from Bath, also used since Roman times. Bath is a most beautiful city of limestone buildings. It was in 1715 that Ralph Allen came to Bath, and realised the great potential there was in the Bath stone. In 1725, the River Avon was made navigable to Bristol and Allen commenced the systematic quarrying of limestone at Combe Down and later at Hampton Down. He collaborated with the speculative architects John Wood (1704-1764) and his son John (1727-1782). It was the Woods who built the beautiful buildings in Bath. John Wood senior, who began to build in 1728, had the financial backing of wealthy landowners. The good quality of his work using Bath stone was such that it was not long before the whole city of Bath was graced with streets and squares, and rows of houses, laid out with great skill and elegance. Particularly noteworthy are the Circus built in 1754 by John Wood senior, with houses embellished with pillars of Corinthian, Doric and Ionic orders; and the Royal Crescent built in 1769 by his son with its beautiful crescent of stone houses adorned with a colonnade of Ionic pillars, and supporting a cornice with a rich entablature. There are other streets of note where buildings of stone can be studied, like Queen's Square, Lansdown Crescent, Cavendish Crescent, Camden, Portland and Somerset Places, Paragon, Belmont, and Belvedere.

A lot of the stone came from the Combe Down quarries where working was both opencast and by underground mining, but the other quarries in Bath are now closed, and Bath stone now comes mainly from quarries in Box and Corsham. In the early days the stone from Box and Corsham was transported by wagon to Bath, and from there by barge to Bristol where much was exported. Although oolitic limestone of the Jurassic period from Box and Corsham and as far as Bradford-on-Avon in Wiltshire had been used for many hundreds of years, it was the completion of the Box Tunnel on the Great Western Railway in 1841 that led to the great expansion of quarrying in the area. The two most important quarries now operating are at Monks Park, Corsham, which is the remaining example of underground mining in the area; the other is the Hazelbury quarry where the stone is recovered by open cast working. A view of this latter quarry is shown in Figure 5. Figure 6 shows blocks of limestone being hauled to the surface at the Monks Park quarry, from a depth of eighty feet or so below. There are many disused mines in the district like Long Platt mine, Clift mine, Hawthorne mine, Holly Bush mine, Wansdyke, Park Lane, Ridge mine, Elm Park and others, but one of the most famous was St Aldhelm's quarry at Box.

Legend has it that St Aldhelm (645-709 AD) founded the abbey at Malmesbury and chose the stone at Box for building it. He also used it for St Lawrence church at Bradford-on-Avon, one of the oldest churches in England. There are a great number of small opencast quarries, many now disused from which stone for local building has been obtained, and for

Fig. 5 Hazelbury Quarry.

Fig. 6 Monks Park Quarry.
(Photo by permission of Kingston Minerals Ltd)

walling and tiling, stretching right across the stone belt from Bath and Bradford-on-Avon to Malmesbury.

Some limestone was quarried at Swindon, and what is now the Town Garden was once a quarry producing Purbeck-type limestone. Not far away in Okus Road, Portland-type stone of the same age was worked from a quarry, the geological section of which can still be seen. Similar stone was quarried at Brill in Buckinghamshire and may be the northern limit of the Portland and Purbeck beds.

Further south in Wiltshire, stone described as sandy glauconite limestone of the Jurassic Portland beds has for many years been mined at Chilmark. It was used in the thirteenth century for the construction of Salisbury Cathedral. Stone of similar type is still quarried at Tucking Mill quarry to the west of Tisbury, and is particularly valuable for restoration work. Chilmark and Tisbury stone have been used for many local buildings, and particularly churches, like that at Teffont Evias.

Diverting far eastward into Surrey around Godalming, Bargate stone of the Lower Greensand is found. The Lower Greensand occurs between the Wealden clay and the Gault deposits. The stone

Fig. 7 Painswick.

has been obtained from quarries near Godalming, at Compton, Holloway Hill, Huntmore and Northbrook. Bargate stone contains a large amount of sand and in some layers becomes practically a sandstone. It is therefore a very variable material. In Kent from the Hythe beds of the Lower Greensand is an even more siliceous limestone, known as Kentish Rag. It is quarried at Borough Green, and in times past at many places in the Maidstone area from Aylesford in the north to Boughton in the south. It was used by the Romans and can be seen in the lower courses of London Wall. Being very tough the stone is difficult to work. In the fourteenth century Kentish Ragstone from Aylesford was used for the water gate of the Tower of London,

for Old St Paul's, Leeds Castle and Eltham Palace. In the weald of Kent from Maidstone to Hindhead cottages built with ragstone can be seen. Stone from the Boughton quarries and from Folkestone quarry was used for Dover Castle in the thirteenth century, and for Sheppey Castle in the following century.

Returning westward into Gloucester one comes back to the Jurassic Oolitic limestone. Important quarries are at Campden, whence stone for the West Front and New Tower of Llandaff Cathedral was obtained; at Naunton, near Cheltenham; at Guiting, which supplied stone for St John's College, Christ Church, and Balliol College, Oxford; at Painswick, whence came the stone for rebuilding St George's Cathe-

18

dral, Southwark. Painswick stone was, in fact, used as far back as about 1200 for Gloucester Cathedral, and later for All Hallows by the Tower, in London; for the interior of Arundel Castle, and that of York Guildhall; and for new vaulting at the Deanery, Westminster. The town of Painswick, built almost entirely with local stone, is well worth a visit. A fragment is shown in Figure 7. Stone once quarried at Northleach was used for the church of SS Peter and Paul, Northleach, and a nearby quarry at Farmington supplied stone for rebuilding the Inner Temple Church, London.

In Oxfordshire there have been many important quarries of oolitic limestone. Stone from the Bladon quarries was used for the random course walling in the New Bodleian Library at Oxford. Taynton supplied stone in the thirteenth century for Woodstock and in the following century for St George's Chapel, Windsor. Headington stone was used to a great extent in Oxford; for example in the fifteenth century tower of Merton College, and for Magdalen College. Unfortunately Headington stone tends to exfoliate, and decay, and in consequence repairs have had to be made with other limestones like that from Bladon or Clipsham from Rutland. Hornton stone from the Edgehill quarry not far from Banbury is a ferruginous limestone and its brown and blue grey colour is reflected in the appearance of buildings of the district, particularly those in Banbury.

Throughout the whole of the Cotswold area, there are many beautiful towns and villages built practically entirely of the oolitic limestone; places like Broadway with its wide street lined with beautiful stone buildings, Burford,

Fig. 8 Arlington Row, Bibury.

Stow-in-the Wold, Stanway, Bourton-on-the-Water, Lower Slaughter, Painswick and many more. A sketch of some town houses in Painswick is in Figure 7 already referred to. Some smaller cottages at Arlington Row, Bibury, are shown in the sketch in Figure 8. Stone from Burford, of smooth texture, and easily carved, was used by Sir Christopher Wren for interior work at St Paul's Cathedral.

In Warwickshire there are many quarries no longer working, at Bearley, Bidford, Harbury, Grafton Court,. Newbold-on-Avon, Princethorpe, Stretton, Upton and other places.

Aynho in Northamptonshire is one of the most beautiful stone villages in England. Further east, near Corby, are the famous Weldon quarries producing oolitic limestone of the Jurassic series, sometimes referred to as Lincolnshire limestone. As early as the thirteenth century, Weldon stone was used in Rockingham Castle, and later for King's College Chapel in Cambridge. The stone is a warm cream to pale buff colour. Another quarry now no longer working producing stone similar to the Weldon variety, was at Kings Cliffe. Not far away is Colleyweston where limestone, the same geologically as Weldon stone, but of a fissile nature, has been quarried extensively and used for roof tiling. The stone is normally quarried in large blocks which are allowed to weather during the winter, with the bedding planes vertical. Rain penetrates between the layers and in frosty weather the expanding ice so formed splits the blocks into plates of suitable thickness for shaping into roofing tiles.

In the village of Barnack, also not far from Stamford, some excellent limestone was quarried as far back as the Roman period, and was later exten-

sively used by the Norman builders. It was used in many early English buildings, as for example the Abbey at Bury St Edmunds, and at Ely Cathedral for some of the carved doorways. Another very famous oolitic limestone comes from quarries at Clipsham near Oakham in Rutland. It is creamy buff in colour, and sometimes has blue patches, and has been used widely in many famous buildings, particularly for repairs and restoration work at several cathedrals like Canterbury, Peterborough, Ripon and Salisbury, and at York Minster; for restoration work at the Houses of Parliament, Buckingham Palace and Hampton Court Palace; and extensively in Oxford at most of the colleges to replace Headington stone which has decayed. Recent buildings using Clipsham stone are the new House of Commons, Guildford Cathedral, and Nuffield College, Oxford.

Continuing to follow the limestone belt into Lincolnshire some other important oolitic limestones (Lincolnshire limestone) deposits are found. At Ancaster the working face of the quarry is up to thirty feet in depth and produces two main types of stone. The stone from the upper layers is a shelly limestone known as Ancaster Weathered, brown and bluish brown in colour and useful for paving. It has a beautiful patterning and when polished is used for interior work. The stone from the lower layers is a more compact stone of medium grain and known as Ancaster Freestone and is particularly suitable for elaborately carved work. A very good type of Lincolnshire limestone is quarried at Ketton, near Stamford. It is fine grained, and although soft when quarried hardens on exposure. It has been used very extensively, and it is only possible to mention a few of the many buildings where it has been employed. In Cambridge it was used for Wren's Library at Trinity; all the original part of Downing College; and for the colleges of Caius and Gonville, Downing and Emanuel. The façade of the City Hall of Norwich and the chapel at Haileybury College are other examples. It has been used for repair work at Westminster School and, like Clipsham, at Buckingham Palace. The very beautiful tower and spire of the Early English Church at Ketton is built with the local stone. Similar oolitic limestone, referred to as Casterton Freestone or Stamford Freestone, is dug at Casterton. Some layers of this stone, known as Stamford Limestone marble, can be polished and used for interior work.

Lincoln Cathedral is an outstanding example of the use of limestone. The stone comes from the cathedral's own quarry to the north of the cathedral, on the road to Brigg. Several grades of stone are dug; the upper or white bed gives a fine textured stone, easily carved, and the lower or silver bed contains fossils and can be used for paving.

To the west and north, in Derbyshire and Yorkshire and into Westmoreland, there are deposits of carboniferous, or mountain limestone. One quarry is at Coalhill in Derbyshire, but in earlier times many other quarries were worked in Ashover, Buxton, Culver and Crich. Similar stone, light brown to dark grey in colour with fossil markings, is quarried in Deepdale in North Yorkshire, while in Westmoreland at Orton Scar, and Crosby in Ravensworth Fell, carboniferous limestone, fawn or red in colour, with calcite veining is quarried. Incidentally in Wales, the quarry at Penmon, near Beaumaris in Anglesey also produces carboniferous limestone.

Dolomitic, or magnesian limestone from the Permian series is obtained in North Yorkshire. The Huddlestone quarry at Sherburn-in-Elmet, owned by York Minster, is famous. As far back as 1434 this stone was used at York Minster and is being used for the current restoration work. In 1442 it was used in the Henry VII Chapel at Westminster. A quarry at Hovingham, also in North Yorkshire, provides a creamy white oolitic limestone of the Corallian series.

Another type of limestone which should be mentioned is known as 'clunch'. It is a very hard form of chalk containing some calcite, and has been used for many centuries, particularly by church builders for internal work. Having a uniform texture it could be worked and carved easily. However it does not weather well and consequently it has not been used externally to any appreciable extent. Two of the finest examples of its use are the interior of St Mary's Church, Luton, and the beautiful and intricately carved and ornate arcading of the fourteenth century Lady Chapel at Ely Cathedral. The stone occurs sporadically, often as outcrops along the edge of the chalk belt extending from the Chiltern Hills in Buckinghamshire to Hunstanton on the north coast of Norfolk. It was quarried at Totternhoe near Dunstable in Bedfordshire, and in Cambridgeshire at Barrington, Burwell, Cherryhinton, Eversden, Haslingfield, Islesham, Reach and elsewhere. It occurs in outcrops in the west and north-west of Norfolk and has been used locally for the walls of many farm buildings and cottages.

21

Sandstone Quarries

The most important areas for sandstone are in Salop, Derbyshire, West Yorkshire, and the Forest of Dean (Figure 2). There are however less extensive deposits elsewhere which provide valuable stone for building. There is, for example, the cretaceous sandstone of Sussex, which occurs principally at Fittleworth near Little Bognor in the Hythe beds of the Lower Greensand, and at West

tiles. The slabs of stone are laid on a relatively low-pitched roof on account of the weight. Slabs of stone are also placed above the windows and form the roof of the porch. Further east in the North Downs of Surrey there is a calcareous sandstone known as Reigate, Gatton, Merstham, or Malmestone. It was used as far back as the Norman period, often as a substitute for Caen stone from France and much favoured

Fig. 9 Horsham tiled roof at Ockley.

Fig. 10 Sandstone wall of Coldharbour, Surrey.

Hoathly, near East Grinstead in the Hastings beds of the Wealden series. The town of Horsham is midway between Fittleworth and West Hoathly, and in consequence the sandstone from the neighbourhood is often referred to as Horsham stone. The colour varies from blue-brown to honey. Apart from its use in walls, some of it splits readily to produce paving slabs and more importantly roofing tiles which are in general much thicker and heavier than the well-known Cotswold tiles. Figure 9 shows a house at Ockley near Leith Hill roofed with Horsham

by the Norman builders — but was slightly greyer in colour.

Figure 10 shows a wall at Coldharbour close by Leith Hill in Surrey, to the north of Horsham, consisting of the local sandstone. The random bonding is noteworthy, and the insertion of small fragments of iron slag in the joints, just visible at the upper right-hand side of the photograph, appears to be a local tradition.

The stone can be seen at the Tower of London, for example in the crypt of the Wakefield Tower, in parts of Westminster Abbey and St Stephen's

22

Chapel, in the crypt of the Guildhall, London, and in many of the old City churches. Large quantities were used for the Palace of Nonsuch, at Cheam, between Sutton and Epsom, built by Henry VIII.

In the Bristol and Forest of Dean areas the Pennant sandstones are very important and widely used. There are a large number of quarries many of which, however, are no longer working. Many years ago the stone was dug in the county of Gloucester at Frampton-Cotterall, Iron Acton, Mangotsfield, Stapleton and Winterbourne. Geologically sandstones of the Forest of Dean belong to the Old Red sandstone (Devonian) and Carboniferous periods. Quarries of Old Red sandstone have been worked between Mitcheldean and Longhope, to the west of Gloucester, and the material used for many local churches and houses. In the Forest of Dean quarries are operating in the Coleford area, at Barnhill producing grey stone, at Bixhead blue stone, and at Cannop grey-pink stone. Barnhill grey stone has been used recently for Berkeley nuclear power station. Many thousands of tons of stone from quarries along the Wye Valley have been used in the construction of the walls protecting the banks of the River Severn and extending almost continuously from Avonmouth to Gloucester. Some of the villages in the Forest of Dean, for example in the neighbourhood of Lydney like Aylburton, built with brown and red sandstone have a rather sombre appearance.

Blue Pennant stone is quarried at Gelligaer Common in Ebbw Vale. It was used in Norman times for building the castle at Caerphilly, a few miles to the south, and that town has many picturesque buildings built of the same material. Further to the west in the Cambrian mountain region the sandstone varies from a silvery grey to a rich purple colour and is well demonstrated at St David's Cathedral and the neighbouring buildings. Stone for the cathedral was obtained locally at Nolton Haven and from the cliffs of Caerfai and Caebwdy.

Returning into England and proceeding northwards into Northamptonshire, sandstone, varying in colour from cream to brown, of the Jurassic system is obtained from quarries operating at New Duston and Moulton. A diversion to the eastern counties to Norfolk reveals a deposit of ferruginous sandstone of the Lower Greensand. It is still quarried at Snettisham and is often known as Carstone. It is golden brown in colour. Similar stone is sometimes quarried where it outcrops in the Isle of Ely. It was used in foundations and in the hearting of walls at Ely Cathedral.

In Nottinghamshire dolomitic or magnesian sandstone is obtained. Two types, white and red, are quarried at Mansfield, the former weathering better than the latter. There is also a true red sandstone. As far back as the middle of the fourteenth century stone quarried close to the castle at Nottingham was used for repairs to that building. In Salop, a whitish grey sandstone of the Triassic period known as Keuper sandstone, has been quarried at Grinshill about eight miles to the north of Shrewsbury. A similar stone was at one time quarried in the Swinney mountain, near Oswestry and in the Bowden quarry near Munslow. Sandstone is widely used throughout the county. Ludlow Castle, on the southern border of Salop, is built with a yellowish-grey sandstone of the Silurian system and in the Church Stretton area there are many picturesque villages built with similar sandstone, the appearance of which is often enhanced by the purple and greenish streaks within it. The Romans employed the local grey sandstone for building their city of Viroconium at Wroxeter, near Shrewsbury; while Shrewsbury itself has many later buildings which are mostly of red sandstone.

In Cheshire, sandstones of the Millstone Grit series of the Carboniferous system become prominent particularly in the Macclesfield area, where quarries at Kerridge and Rainow are producing stone of varying shades of colour from pink to fawny-grey. All over the West Midlands the Keuper sandstones are abundant, and have been used for many buildings in the Birmingham area and northwards through Newcastle-under-Lyme up to Chester. Here the city and the surrounding villages have many buildings of pink Keuper sandstone, the cathedral providing an excellent example of its use.

In Staffordshire, the famous Hollington stone of the Triassic system is still quarried in considerable quantities at Hollington and Tean a few miles to the northwest of Uttoxeter. There were other quarries, now disused, in the area from Sedgley and Bilston to Stafford, and particularly at Brewood and Tixall. Hollington stone varies in colour from white and pink to red. The pinkish stone was used for Hereford Cathedral, and more recenlty for Coventry Cathedral.

Derbyshire abounds in sandstone and there are in fact so many quarries throughout the Peak District working, and many disused, that it is difficult to select a few to mention here. To the

west and north of Matlock there are important quarries at Darley Dale, Birchover, Elton and Stanton Moor; to the north of Bakewell and at Bakewell itself are those at Hathersage and Grindleford; to the south-west of Chesterfield at Wingerworth; at Chinley Moor near Whaley Bridge and at Birch Vale nearer to Stockport. Geologically, the sandstone from all the sites mentioned belongs to the Carboniferous Millstone Grit series, except the Birch Vale and the Wingerworth sandstones which belong to the Carboniferous Coal Measures series.

The stone generally is very durable, and close grained. It weathers well in the industrial cities of the north. Some grades split fairly readily to produce paving slabs and flags for roofing. The latter are heavy rather like the Horsham tiles and are laid at a low pitch. The sandstone ranges widely in colour from pink, yellow, buff, grey to blue and mauve, and has been so widely used that it is difficult to single out any particular examples for special mention. However, as an example, mention might be made of the Birchover sandstone from Darley Dale, which has been used in the construction of the Claerwen Dam in Rhayader, for the Newport Civic Centre, and for the courts and terraces at Nottingham University.

Sandstone of excellent quality abounds throughout the Yorkshire counties, but the largest concentration of quarries now operating is in West Yorkshire. However, there are many quarries often now disused towards the east as near Richmond, particularly on Gatherly Moor; near Boroughbridge; in the neighbourhood of Whitby; and all over the Eastern Moorlands.

The concentration of quarries around Halifax, Huddersfield, Bradford and

Leeds is significant. The sandstone is obtained from two geological strata, the Carboniferous Coal measures, and the Carboniferous Millstone Grit series. Of the former type the stone called Elland Flags is important. The quarries from which it comes are situated not only at Elland Edge and Shepley, near Huddersfield, but at Swales Moor, Southowram and Northowram Hills around Halifax, and at Fairweather Green, Haworth and Eccleshill near Bradford. Some other grades of sandstone from the Coal measures are Gaisby Rock from Bolton Woods, near Bradford, Ackworth Rock, from Ackworth near Pontefract, and Grenoside Rock from Shepley, near Huddersfield. The famous York stone comes mainly from the Shepley area.

Of the sandstones from the Millstone Grit series, the Waterholes Grit from the quarries at Wellfield and Waterholes, near Huddersfield, is important. The Rough Rock from Bramley Fall, near Leeds is also well known and occurs again at Mount Tabor, near Halifax and at Honley and Wellfield near Huddersfield. The quarries at Stancliffe have also produced excellent stone.

York stone is exceedingly hard and durable. Some of it can be split for roofing tiles. Flags are also produced and very widely used for copings, sills, steps and staircases. It has, however, been widely used since early times for paving floors, as in London at Westminster Hall, the rebuilt Guildhall, the Bank of England, the Tower of London and the Royal Palaces. The list is far too long to mention, but other important and more recent buildings of note in which York stone has been used include the Admiralty Buildings, the Royal College of Science, South Kensington, Bristol University, Guildford Cathedral, Huddersfield Town Hall and Manchester Exchange.

The Yorkshire sandstone or Grit stone as it is sometimes called, consists of sand, mainly of quartz or siliceous grains, cemented with silica, iron oxide and carbonate of lime. It ranges in colour from cream, very light brown, golden brown to blue and grey. In very early times it was used at Fountains and Kirkstall, and other Cistercian abbeys in the north of England. In fact many of the stone quarries were owned by the early monks. At Meaux Abbey for example the monks owned a quarry at Brantingham, near Hull, in the twelfth century. Other ancient quarries were at Pontefract, supplying stone for St Stephen's Chapel, Westminster as far back as 1343 and for Windsor Castle the following year. In Nidderdale and Wensley Dale and in the other dales of Yorkshire are many pretty villages, such as Aysgarth, Bainbridge, and Castle Bolton in Nidderdale and Wensley Dale, Arncliffe in Littondale and Burnsall in Wharfdale.

The Millstone Grit, much of it fissile and used for rough walling, paving and roofing, persists throughout the counties north of Yorkshire. In Lancashire there are important quarries of sandstone, at Whitworth, near Rochdale producing blue fissile stone; at Whittle-le-Woods, near Chorley, and at Woolton and Rainhill. Stone from this last quarry, crimson in colour, was used for Liverpool Cathedral. In the county of Durham the creamy brown Dunhouse sandstone from quarries at Winston, near Darlington is important. It was used for the restoration of Durham Cathedral and Castle. Other stone, varying in colour from light buff to brown and grey comes from quarries at Springwell near Gateshead, and at

Stainton and Egglestone, near Barnard Castle. The Blaxter sandstone from a quarry near Elsdon was used at Durham University and for the National Library of Scotland at Edinburgh. Other deposits are still worked in Northumberland at Darney near West Woodburn, at Doddington near Wooler, at Slaley near Hexham, and at Prudham near Fourstones.

In Cumbria, New Red sandstone abounds. It occurs principally in the Penrith area and in consequence is known as Penrith sandstone. It is of Permian age, and bright red in colour; and has been used freely in the town of Penrith with very attractive results. St Bees sandstone of the Triassic period is quarried at Bank End near St Bees. Other deposits of sandstone occur at Kirby Stephen, Kirklinton and Appleby. New Red sandstone has been extensively quarried since the Romans used it for constructing Hadrian's Wall. Many of the buildings in Carlisle are built with it, and from quarries in the neighbourhood of Whitehaven large quantities of sandstone were shipped to Ireland, the Isle of Man and Scotland.

Slate Quarries

The quarries for slates are grouped mainly in three areas of England and Wales (Figure 3).
(a) Devon and Cornwall, particularly along the north coast region, notably at Delabole, although there are many disused quarries along the south coast.
(b) In Cumbria and Lancashire particularly in the Lake District, at Broughton Moor, near Coniston, Buttermere and Burlington near Kirby-in-Furness.
(c) In North Wales from Bangor and

Caernarvon veins; in the Nantile Valley; at Dinorwic; Penrhyn and Vronlog; from the Festiniog or Portmadoc veins; and from the Corris or Aberdovey veins, particularly at Machynlleth. Until recently slates were also quarried in the Prescelly mountains close to the Pembrokeshire-Carmarthen border.

Looking at the quarries in more detail, those in Devon and Cornwall will be dealt with first. The largest and most celebrated slate quarries in Cornwall are at Delabole, in the parish of St Teath on the north coast between Stratton and Padstow. The Old Delabole quarry is over a mile round and several hundred feet deep and produces grey to greygreen slates of the Devonian system. The quarry has been worked since the reign of Elizabeth I and large quantities of slate were exported from Port Isaac. The Trebarwith and Trecarne quarries at Delabole produce multicoloured slate, reddish brown and bluegrey.

At Tintagel not far from Delabole a green slate of chlorite phyllite is quarried, and at Lower Penpethy, near Tintagel greygreen and silvergrey slate of the Devonian system is quarried. There are also ancient quarries at Trevalga nearby. In earlier times there were numerous quarries in other areas particularly between Liskeard and the River Tamar, around Lostwithiel, Golant and Fowey.

There are numerous places in Devon where slates have been obtained. Between Plymouth and Tavistock, at Bere Ferres there was a slate quarry operating as far back as the thirteenth century, and there are now quarries working at Moorshop and Mill Hill producing slates of various shades of colour varying from blue to brown. Nearer

Fig. 11 The Nunnery, Dunster.

Plymouth, at Plympton, many slates were produced last century at Cann quarry on the banks of the River Plym. The quarry belonged to the Earl of Morley and the slates were conveyed to Plymouth by canal and railway. There were also many slate quarries between Plymouth and Dartmouth, particularly around Kingsbridge, and in the valley of the River Yealm. At Charleton nearby the quarries were working in mediaeval times.

In Somerset slate was obtained at the Tracebridge quarry, Treborough, and at Oakhampton quarry, Wivelscombe in the Brendon Hills; and further east at Rooks Castle, to the southwest of Bridgewater. Some of the North Somerset slates can be seen cladding the front of the Nunnery at Dunster, shown in Figure 11.

Proceeding northward, at Swithland, east of the Charnwood Forest, large quantities of rather thick and heavy slates were quarried and appear to have been used since Roman times. Further north still in Lancashire, slate quarries, many disused, abound. Blue slate occurs chiefly in the rocky mountainous tracts in the northern parts of High Furness. Well-known Burlington Blue Grey slate is quarried at Kirby-in-Furness. Bursting Stone quarry and Moss Rigg quarry at Tilberthwaite, near Coniston are working and producing the Lakeland Green slates. The Green Buttermere slates of Cumbria are also famous, and produced at the Honister quarry near Keswick, but slates have also in the past been quarried at Bassenthwaite, Borrowdale, Cockermouth and Ulpha. In the western mountains are vast quantities of slate of various colours.

Westmoreland Green slates have been used extensively in many towns. In London, for example, they can be seen at Kensington Palace, St James's Palace, Westminster Hall, Imperial College of Science and Technology, Chelsea Hospital and Queen Mary College. Other quarrying areas are Langdale, Coniston and Ambleside. Kirkstone at the summit of Kirkstone, Brathay near Ambleside, Broughton Moor near Coniston, and Elterwater and Spoutcrag in Langdale are important quarries. The shades of colour of the slates vary from light green, olive green, silvery green and even blue black at Brathay.

Important and extensive slate quarries occur in North Wales, around Blaenau Festiniog, Talysarn, Dinorwic, Bethesda and Corris. In the Blaenau Festiniog area are the quarries of Maen Offeren, Llechwedd and Cwt-y-Bugail producing blue-grey slates. Portmadoc has long been the port of export and to facilitate transport a two-foot narrow gauge line was laid between that town and Dduallt close to Blaenau Festiniog nine and a half miles away. Although the railway has not been used for transporting slates since 1938 it now carries passengers and is known as the Festiniog Railway. It is privately owned. Festiniog is a depressingly grim town of stone cottages and is surrounded by vast heaps of slate waste.

In the Talysarn area the quarry at Twll Llwyd is important, and produces slates of varying shades of colour from green to reddish brown. Nearly all the quarries of Pen-yr-Orsedd and Twll Coed are producing green slates.

The quarries at Dinorwic, not far from Llanberis, another rather drab mountain town with vast quantities of slate waste around it, have been important. In the Bethesda area the Penrhyn quarries are still operating, producing green and grey slates. To the east, in the Horse Shoe Pass near Llangollen, deep blue slates are obtained from the Clogau quarries. In Montgomeryshire are the Aberllefenni and Braichgoch quarries near Corris producing blue slates.

In all the areas mentioned a great many disused quarries have left unsightly scars on the countryside, which is also disfigured by vast heaps of slate waste.

There is hardly a town or village in England and Wales which does not have some buildings roofed with slate. The material has been so widely distributed that it is difficult to single out any particular buildings for mention.

A block of slate can be easily split by hammer and chisel along the cleavage planes into a number of laminae, and generally the thinner they are, the better is the quality and durability of the tile. The principal minerals present in slates are various compounds of silica and alumina such as chlorites, felspar, muscovite, and quartz, but there may be in lesser quantities others such as magnetitie, pyrites, sulphide of iron marcasite and calcite (calcium carbonate); this last being detrimental if the tiles are to be used in an urban atmosphere, as sulphur fumes may attack the calcite to form calcium sulphate, and in doing so may scale or split the tiles.

Granite Quarries

The term 'granite' is used here in its wide and generally accepted meaning as applied by the stone industry. Dealing first with the group of granite quarries in Devon and Cornwall, their main concentrations occur in the area stretching from Bodmin Moor, down towards the Lizard, and around Dartmoor and the region extending southwards to the coast. Quarries at present operating are listed in Table 5, but there are of course a great many quarries no longer used, or worked out, or only used sporadically. Granite, or moorstone, is also abundant on the surface of the moors and has been used in great quantities since remote times for building houses and churches throughout Cornwall. The remains of many prehistoric structures in the form of hut circles, built with blocks of granite, have survived. One of the better examples is to be seen at Chysauster which certainly dates back to the second century BC. A sketch of it is shown in Figure 19.

Most of the Cornish granite is silver grey in colour and of medium or fine grain. As with most igneous rocks the material is not easily cut, or dressed, but with modern appliances it can be cut into relatively thin slabs and polished, and used for the decorative cladding of buildings. One example of this use is seen at the Trades Union Congress memorial building in London. Tor Down granite from St Breward, Bodmin was used. Generally, however, granite is used in large rectangular blocks with rough hewn surfaces, with little decoration. Notable examples of its use are old Waterloo Bridge, now demolished, built with Penrhyn granite, and almost all the more recent Thames bridges from Tower Bridge to Kew; and for the South Bank also using Penrhyn granite. Bridges in other parts have employed granite, as for example the Severn Bridge, linking Aust with Chepstow where granite from the De Lank quarry at St Breward, Bodmin was used for the copings to the piers and cutwaters; and material from the same source was used for the bridge over the Tamar spanning between St

Brideaux and Saltash and linking Devon and Cornwall.

Other buildings of note built with Cornish granite are the Metropolitan Cathedral in Liverpool and Central Hall, Westminster where material from the Pelastine quarry at Penhryn was used. Although the granite in the examples quoted was silver grey in colour, several other varieties have been worked, but not very extensively. Luxulyan granite composed of black tourmaline and pink felspar was used for the Wellington Sarcophagus in St Paul's Cathedral, London.

The area around Plymouth on the border between Cornwall and Devon, and on Dartmoor, abounds in granite quarries many of which are no longer worked. Some of the quarries are very ancient. Transportation of the heavy granite blocks has always been a problem, and to facilitate this Sir Thomas Tyrwhitt had a railroad track laid at the beginning of the last century, which enabled the material to be carried from the Princetown area of Dartmoor, down to the Sutton Pool in Plymouth, a distance of twenty-four miles, whence it could be conveyed by boat to its required destination. There are big granite quarries in the Ashburton district of Dartmoor. Those to the east of Haytor Rocks, near Bovey Tracy provided the stone, over a hundred years ago, for the British Museum and General Post Office in London, and for London Bridge, now demolished. The granite was conveyed to London by boat from Teignmouth, having been brought down from the quarries on a tramway, built in 1820, a distance of six miles, to the head of a canal constructed in 1794. Thence it was shipped by barge to Teignmouth. The tramway is no longer in use.

The origin of the vast granite mass of Dartmoor is of great interest. It was formed by the cooling and solidification of lava derived from deep down in the earth, and once fed the Carboniferous and Post Carboniferous volcanoes of Devon.

Granite of a different colour is found in parts of the Midlands and North of England. Red Granite occurs at Mountsorrel in Leicestershire while in Westmoreland the famous Shap granite, a porphyritic granite, varying in shades of colour from brownish red to greyish pink, has provided material for many important works throughout Britain, such as the Queen Elizabeth II Dock, Manchester Ship Canal, and the King George V Graving Dock at Southampton. The main quarries are situated about three miles south of Shap, but from Kendal in the south to Wasdale Crag in the west, and throughout Cumbria, there are many outcrops of granite.

In Wales porphyritic granite, grey or bluish grey in colour is quarried in Merioneth at Arenig near Bala, and in Caernarvonshire at the Eifi quarry at Trevor. This latter granite was used in the construction of locks for the Mersey Docks and Harbour Board at Liverpool.

The Mason's Craft

The mason's craft is one of the oldest and most important of the building crafts. The masons were broadly of two grades, mason hewers (cissores) or cutters (taylatores) and mason layers (legers) or setters (positores). The hewers were adept with the mallet and chisel, working and carving freestone, ie limestone and the finer grained sandstone, in which case they were often called freemasons. In distinction to these freemasons were the hard hewers who were concerned with the preparation of some of the much harder, tougher and intractable varieties of stone like Kentish ragstone. The layers, sometimes called rough masons, or rowmasons (cubitores) were concerned with the preparation of stone, often in the quarry, by hammering or scappling, instead of by cutting with a chisel. On this account they were sometimes called scapplers (batrarii). The layers or setters also laid the stones in the walls, and when doing this they were sometimes referred to as wallers (muratorii) to distinguish them, for example, from the paviors (pavores), whose job it was to lay stone paving. Generally the masons worked in lodges, or workshops, on the building site, under the supervision of the mastermason (magister cementariorum). Strict rules of conduct were laid down, particularly for the apprentices, who after years of training could become journeymen, and in course of time a selected few of them might become mastermasons. The lodge was very much a training ground in craftsmanship, and it was possible for a rough mason, for example, to gain experience and skill and become a freemason. To become a master of his craft a journeyman would have to demonstrate his skill and ability, often by producing a 'masterpiece' of work.

The mastermason was usually responsible for the details of the stonework. He could make rough sketches, plans and elevations, which could be understood by his men; he could estimate quantities of materials, and supervise the workmen. A mastermason, after years of experience, might assume very great importance by becoming a king's mason (cementarius regis). Henry de Yevele (1319-1399) having been a mason for thirty years, mainly at Westminster Abbey, was an excellent example of this attainment. He became king's mason or 'devisor' of masonry, a position, it would seem, akin to an architect. Apart from having oversight of the king's palaces and castles, he acted as adviser or consultant on a number of projects. He served, for example, on the commission which advised on the reconstruction of Rochester Bridge. The building of Guildhall, London, was another project on which he advised. In 1356 he served on a committee which drew up regulations for London masons. He, like some other masons and mastermasons, was also a contractor supplying building stone. This was not such an unnatural thing for masons to do, since not only did some of them open up stone quarries on their own account and hew the stone, but they often worked and shaped the blocks at the quarries and were able to supply prepared material to the building sites in the particular shapes and sizes required, leaving the final dressing and carving to be done on the site.

King Henry III employed several mastermasons, whose responsibility it was to select and supervise groups of masons, and other staff, for particular tasks. They were privileged to wear robes presented to them by the king as a mark of their important office. This practice continued through the mediaeval period. Stonemasons were highly respected people, and often the craft was handed down through successive generations. A few families of stonemasons might be mentioned. The Arnolds, established near Ilminster, were probably typical of provincial families engaged in building crafts.

John and William Arnold worked on the building of Wadham College (1610-1613). William was a mastermason, who prepared plans and superintended the building workers. At a later date a member of the Arnold family was first engaged by Inigo Jones, and then by Wren as a carver at St Paul's Cathedral. Another family of builders were the Strongs. Timothy Strong from Barrington, near Burford, was the contractor for Cornbury Park, Oxfordshire (1632-1633), designed by Nicholas Stone, the architect. Valentine Strong, son of Timothy, and Simeon Strong were engaged in 1634 on the building of St John's College, Oxford (1631-1636) and Thomas Strong, grandson of Timothy, owned the stone quarries at Burford, and was a mastermason working under Wren in the building of St Paul's Cathedral. As Burford stone was used there by Wren, it may be that

Thomas Strong supplied some of it from his quarries.

Another family of stonemasons were the Grumbolds who owned quarries at Weldon, Northamptonshire. Arthur Grumbold (1603-70) was one of the earliest. He lived in a house in the main street of Weldon which still stands, and bears his initials and the date 1654. One branch of the family went to the quarrying village of Raunds, near Higham Ferrers. Another member of the family was Thomas Grumbold who lived at Cambridge. It was he who built the east and south ranges of Clare College, Cambridge (1638-1642), in the Perpendicular style. Robert Grumbold (1639-1720) his successor, directed the works at Trinity College Library, Cambridge, from 1676 to 1682, working to Wren's design. He also built part of the west wing of Clare College, Cambridge, in 1662-1672, again in the

Fig. 12 Haunt Hill House at Weldon; the home of Humphrey Frisbey, mastermason.

Perpendicular style. The Grumbolds at Weldon were related to another family of stonemasons, the Frisbeys. Elizabeth Grumbold married Humphrey Frisbey the son of another Humphrey Frisbey, a stonemason working at nearby Kings Cliffe. The house in which Humphrey Frisbey lived, which he built in 1643, is still standing, and is known as Haunt Hill House, Weldon. On the south gable are carved the arms of the Mason's Company, and the builder's initials H.F. The house, built of Weldon stone from his own quarry, is shown in the sketch in Figure 12.

The mastermason eventually assumed the status of building contractor, owning the quarries, working the stone, transporting it to the building site and incorporating it in the structure. The well-known contracting firm of John Mowlem developed in this way. John Mowlem, founder of the firm, born in 1798 at Swanage, Dorset, came from a stone-quarrying family. At the age of eighteen he became apprenticed in London to Henry Westmacott, a prominent stonemason and brother of the sculptor Sir John Westmacott. By 1816, he had risen to be foreman for Westmacott and worked on many monumental structures such as the Achilles statue in Hyde Park, the statue of Charles James Fox in Bloomsbury Square, Nelson's tomb in St Paul's Cathedral and on various buildings such as Carlton House and Greenwich Palace, where he supervised the work on the exfoliated capitals for the King Charles Quadrangle. About 1832 John Mowlem started business on his own account selling Purbeck paving slabs, shipped by his quarrying relatives at Swanage to his wharf in London at Pumber Basin, where Victoria Station now stands. The business prospered

and the wharf was moved to Paddington Basin, where John Mowlem imported large quantities of granite chips which were used on London's roads, in addition to the importation of the stone from Purbeck.

Methods of stone quarrying and stone working have changed but little in course of time. Picks, bars and wedges are still used for quarrying the sedimentary stone, as they were many centuries ago, advantage always being taken of the natural bedding planes as the best positions for splitting it. Once the upper surface and one side of an unhewn block has been exposed, it then remains for it to be split off from the back and the other side with wedges, and finally prized off its natural bed. It is then sawn into blocks of convenient sizes and sent to the mason's yard. The igneous rocks have no natural uniform beds and can only be hewn or blasted out in irregular blocks. These are either split with wedges or feathers, or cut by mechanically operated toothless iron bandsaws fed with chilled iron shot. The dressing of the stone is carried out with tools of various types, including the axe, the gab, the scabber, the puncheon, and plain and serrated chisels of different sizes.

To utilize the stone to the best advantage from the point of view of strength and resistance to weathering, it is customary to lay it on its natural bed, if it has one, or in such a way that the natural bed is set at right angles to the direction of the thrust. The stone voussoirs of an arch for example are cut and placed so that their natural bedding planes lie radially.

In Figures 13 to 18 are shown the main types of bond used today in stone walls. The common, rough uncoursed, or random rubble wall shown in Figure

Fig. 13 Common rough uncoursed or random rubble.

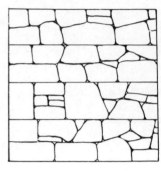

Fig. 14 Random rubble built to course.

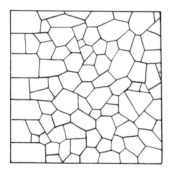

Fig. 15 Polygonal random rubble with hammer-dressed joints.

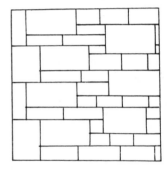

Fig. 16 Irregular coursed, snecked or squared random rubble.

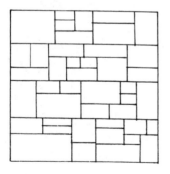

Fig. 17 Random rubble built to courses with beds horizontal and joints vertical.

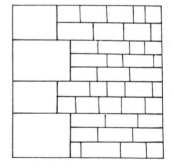

Fig. 18 Coursed rubble.

13, is made of odd-shaped pieces of rock, very often pieces of naturally weathered rock, and it is probably only at the quoins that they need to be dressed. Random rubble, built to course, as shown in Figure 14, makes a stronger wall. Intractable rocks, ragstone and granite for example which fractures into odd shapes can be utilised in polygonal random rubble. In the best work the surfaces are hammer dressed to give close joints as shown in Figure 15. Random rubble walls in which the stones are squared but of irregular size, with small stones or snecks introduced to break the course, as shown in Figure 16, are common in Scotland and this type of work is called snecked rubble. Squared random rubble brought to course is shown in Figure 17, and the last example in Figure 18 shows coursed rubble of squared stone laid in courses to suit the heights of the cornerstones, or rybats.

The work involved in preparing stone blocks for building is considerable and costly, and it is now common practice, even in areas such as the Cotswolds where natural stone is so prolific, for the stone to be crushed at the quarry and used with a binding material, such as Portland cement, to produce precast blocks.

Surface Stones and Erratics used for Building

There are many erratics* and surface stones which have been used locally for building. This is particularly so in the

* The term 'erratics' is applied to the large pieces of stone and boulders which have been transported from their original location. This may have occurred by glacial action or by denudation by flooding.

Fig. 19 Prehistoric house at Chysauster, Cornwall.

moorland areas of Devon and Cornwall, Cumbria and Wales. Many examples of prehistoric hutments and megalithic structures can be seen, notably on Dartmoor. The stone houses at Chysauster, Cornwall, one of which is shown in Figure 19, were erected during the period 200 BC to 300 AD. Here the walls are dry built using boulders of granite gathered from the surface of the moors.

In some chalk areas, as in Wiltshire, there are many sarsens, large sandstone boulders, often known as Druid stones or Bride stones, which have been left on the surface after erosion of the soil and chalk. They are particularly prolific on the surface of the downs, or half buried, in an area called Grey Wethers near Marlborough, and in the valleys around the Fyfield Downs. The stones have been used in many houses and farm buildings in the Avebury and West Overton area. Some of the very large Sarsens, often weighing many tons, were transported for use at Stonehenge, for the Avebury prehistoric circle and the West Kennet long barrow. In years past there was quite an industry carried out on the downs, to break up the sarsens to produce building blocks, while small pieces were shaped and used in neighbouring towns like Swindon, Marlborough and Devizes for curbing stones and cobbles. The so-called 'blue stones' at Stonehenge are similar geologically to material in the Prescelly mountains of South Wales, and were most likely eroded from that area and carried southward by glacial action.

In East Anglia where there is a dearth of building stone, flint walling has been used since the Roman occupation. The walls were built with layers of flint nodules bedded in lime mortar,

Types of flint walling from Cromer, Norfolk

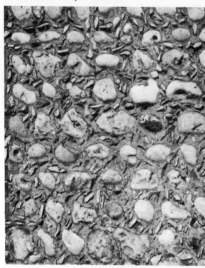

Fig. 20 Undressed flints galleted joints.

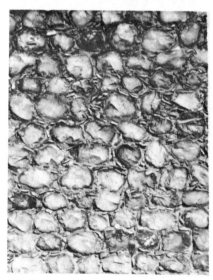

Fig. 21 Knapped flints with galleted joints.

36

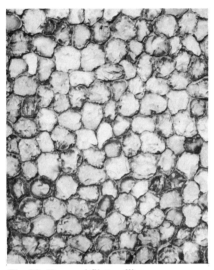

Fig. 22 **Knapped flint walling.**

Fig. 23 Square flint walling.

sometimes split to give a fair face. The finest flintwork is to be seen in Suffolk and Norfolk, the home of flint knapping. The freshly knapped flints derived from the chalk are grey in colour. The example shown in Figure 23, at the parish church of SS Peter and Paul, Cromer, is of the Early Perpendicular period and shows how skilfully the flints were squared so that they could be laid and fitted together with the thinnest of joints. Three other types of flint walling, also at Cromer, show in Figure 20 undressed flints set with galleted joints, in Figure 21 knapped nodules also laid in courses with galleted joints, and in Figure 22 knapped flints skilfully laid in reticulate pattern. The craft of flint knapping for facing rubble walls, flourished in the fifteenth and sixteenth centuries. In East Anglia great use was made also of flint for decorative infillings in association with stonework on walls and buttresses. The gatehouse of the historic priory of St Osyth's, Colchester, is one of the finest examples of this technique; but flint chequered work is also excellent on the walls of the Guildhalls at Kings Lynn and Norwich. In the chalk areas of the southern counties, well away from the coast, it is not uncommon to see chequered flint and chalk walls for cottages. In Wiltshire there are numerous examples in the villages around Salisbury such as Tilshead, Shrewton and Fittleton.

All around the coast can be seen many instances of the use of undressed flints. The flints from the seashore are usually ochreous in colour, but inland, the field flints are whitish or grey.

In conclusion, reference must be made to the hundreds of miles of dry stonewalling erected to surround the fields. They abound across Dart-

37

moor and Exmoor, and all through the Cotswold and limestone area; in Wales, the Lake District, Derbyshire, Yorkshire and further north in Cumbria. Drystone walling is a subject to be studied separately, involving as it does great skill in execution. The techniques vary throughout the country and the two illustrations in Figures 24 and 25 serve merely to demonstrate this point. Figure 24 shows a drywall in the Lake District composed of irregular sand-

Fig. 24 Lakeland drywall.

Fig. 25 Cotswold drywall.

stone blocks interlaced with slates, whereas Figure 25 illustrates the type of wall erected with limestone blocks throughout the Cotswold area.

Appendix

Distribution of Quarries

The outline maps in Figures 1, 2 and 3 show the distribution of stone quarries in England and Wales. The limestone quarries are indicated as 'circles', the sandstone quarries as 'squares', the granite quarries as 'triangles' and the slate quarries as 'diamonds'. Tables 2 to 5 list many of the main quarries still in operation. For more comprehensive and detailed information on working quarries in Great Britain, reference should be made to the *Natural Stone Directory* compiled and published by Park Lane Publications Ltd, London. Many quarries are no longer operating, or if so sporadically. Some of these are very ancient and important historically, and are mentioned in later tables.

Samples of building stones can be seen in the Geological Museum at South Kensington.

A glance at the maps shows that the igneous rocks occur mainly in the western parts of England and Wales, from Cornwall to Cumbria. The sandstones occur for the most part between the igneous rocks and the main limestone range which forms the backbone of England extending practically continuously from Devon to North Yorkshire. To the east of the limestone range the country has very little stone available for building.

A geological classification of building stones at present being quarried is given in Table 1 below. The numbers refer to the particular stones listed in Tables 2, 3, and 4 following.

Table 1.   Geological classification of building stones

	Geological System	Limestone (see Table 2)	Sandstone (see Table 3)	Slate (see Table 4)
Quaternary	Pleistocene			
Tertiary	Pliocene Miocene Oligocene Eocene			
Mesozoic	Cretaceous	43.	1,2,3,9.	
	Jurassic	2,3,5,6,7,8,9 10,11,12,13,14, 15,16,17,18,19, 20,21,22,23,24, 25,26,27,28,29, 30,31,32,33,34, 35,36,37,38,39, 40,41,42,47.	7,8.	
	Triassic		10,15,16,62.	
Palaeozoic	Permian	45.	17,60,61.	
	Carboniferous	1,4,44,46,48.	4,5,6,11,12,13, 14,18,19,20,21, 22,23,25,26,27, 28,29,30,31,32, 33,34,35,36,37, 38,39,40,41,42, 43,44,45,46,47, 48,49,50,51,52, 53,54,55,56,57, 58,59,63,64,65, 66,67,68.	
	Devonian			1,2,3,4,5,6,7, 8,18,21.
	Silurian			9,10,11,12,14, 19,20,22,23,24, 25,26.
	Ordovician			
	Cambrian			13,15,16,17.

Table 2   Limestone quarries still being worked

County	Building Stone		Location
Somerset	1	Battscombe	Cheddar
	2	Box Ground	Box
	3	Blue Lias	Charleton Mackrell
	4	Cheddar	Westbury-sub-Mendip
	5	Combe Down	Bath
	6	Doulting	Doulting
	7	Ham Hill	Ash
	8	Stowey	Bishop Sutton
Dorset	9	Portland Roach	Portland
	10	Portland Stone	Portland
	11	Portland	Sheat
	12	Purbeck	Langton Matravers
	13	do	do
	14	do	do
	15	do	Worth Matravers
	16	do	do
	17	do	do
	18	do	Herston
	19	do	Swanage
Wiltshire	20	Chilmark	Tisbury
	21	Tisbury	West Tisbury
	22	Monks Park	Corsham
Gloucestershire	23	Campden	Campden
	24	Cotswold	Cirencester
	25	do	Naunton
	26	Guiting	Guiting
Oxfordshire	27	Bladon Cotswold	Bladon
	28	Hornton	Edgehill
	29	Taynton	Taynton
Northants	30	Weldon	Weldon
	31	Colleyweston	Colleyweston
	32	do	do
	33	do	do
Cambridgeshire	34	Walling Stone	Helpston Heath
	35	do	Yarwell
	36	do	Wansford
	37	do	do
Leicestershire	38	Clipsham	Oakham
	39	do	do
Lincolnshire	40	Ancaster	Ancaster
	41	Ketton	Ketton
	42	Casterton	Stamford

Table 2   (continued)

County		Building Stone	Location
Kent	43	Kentish Rag	Borough Green
Derbyshire	44	Derbyshire Fossil	Coalhill
North Yorkshire	45	Huddleston	Sherburn-in-Elmet
	46	Deepdale	Dentdale
	47	Hovingham	Hovingham
Cumbria	48	Orton Scar	Orton Scar

Table 3   Sandstone quarries still being worked

County		Building Stone	Location
West Sussex	1	Sussex Sandstone	Little Bognor
	2	do	West Hoathly
	3	Wealden Sussex	do
Gloucestershire	4	Forest of Dean	Barnhill
	5	do	Cannop
	6	do	Coleford
Northants	7	Duston	New Duston
	8	Moulton	Moulton
Norfolk	9	Carstone	Snettisham
Salop	10	Grinshill	Wem
Cheshire	11	Kerridge	Kerridge
	12	do	do
	13	do	do
	14	Rainow	Rainow
Staffordshire	15	Hollington	Hollington
	16	do	do
Nottingham	17	White Mansfield	Mansfield
Derbyshire	18	Birchover	Stanton Moor
	19	Chinley Moor	Hayfield
	20	Darley Dale	Darley Dale
	21	Hall Dale	do
	22	Watts Cliff	Elton
	23	Derbyshire Grit Stone	Birch Vale
	24	Davie Blocks	Bakewell
	25	Delph	Wingerworth
	26	Millstone Edge	Hathersage
	27	Stoke Stone	Grindleford

Table 3 (continued)

County		Building Stone	Location
Great Manchester	28	Britannia	Whitworth
Lancashire	29	Revidge Grit	Chorley
West Yorkshire	30	Bolton Wood	Bradford
	31	do	do
	32	do	do
	33	Hard Rock	Halifax
	34	Yorkshire Delph	Fairweather Green
	35	Yorkshire Flagstone	Bradford
	36	Elland Edge	Southowram
	37	Hard York	Halifax
	38	Hard York Freestone	Northowram
	39	Ringby	Swalesmoor
	40	Yorkshire Freestone	Mount Tabor
	41	York	Rawdon
	42	York Stone	Southowram
	43	do	do
	44	Yorkshire Stone	Halifax
	45	Crosland Hill	Southowram
	46	Greenmoor	Shepley
	47	Hard York	Crosland Hills
	48	Lane Head	Shepley
	49	Waterholes	Waterholes
	50	Wellfield	Wellfield
	51	Bramley Fall	Leeds
	52	Woodkirk	Morley
	53	Elland	Rastrick
	54	York Stone	Holmfirth
Durham	55	Dunhouse	Winston
	56	Stainton	Stainton
	57	Windy Hill	Egglestone
Tyneside	58	Springwell	Springwell
Cumbria	59	Lazonby	Lazonby
	60	Penrith Red	Stonerays
	61	Red St Bees	St Bees
Northumberland	62	Ladycross	Slaley
	63	Blaxter	Elsdon
	64	Darney	West Woodburn
	65	Prudham	Fourstones
	66	Doddington	Wooler
Mid Glamorgan	67	Rassau	Rassau
	68	Pencaemaur	Gelligaer
Dyfed	69	Caerbwdy	St Davids

Table 4   Slate quarries still operating

County	Building Stone		Location
Cornwall	1	Cornish Rustic	Lower Penpethy
	2	Delabole	Delabole
	3	Trebarwith Rustic	do
	4	Trecarne Rustic	Trecarne
	5	Tredinnick Rustic	Tredinnick St Issey
Devon	6	Mill Hill	Mill Hill, Tavistock
	7	Longford Rustic	Moorshop, Tavistock
Clwyd	8	Berwyn	Clogau, Horse Shoe Pass
Gwynedd	9	Blue Grey Slate	Aberllefenni, Corris
	10	Blue Welsh Slate	Braichgoch, Corris
	11	Cwt-y-Bugail	Blaenau-Festiniog
	12	Maen Offeren	do do
	13	Pen-yr-Orsedd	Nantile
	14	Llechwedd	Blaenau-Festiniog
	15	Twll Coed Green	Nantile
	16	Penrhyn	Bethesda
	17	Twll Llwyd	Twll Llwyd
Cumbria	18	Burlington Blue Grey	Kirby-in-Furness
	19	Lakeland Green	Coniston Old Man
	20	do do	Moss Rigg, Tilberthwaite
	21	Brathay	Ambleside
	22	Broughton Moor	Coniston
	23	Spoutcrag	Langdale Valley
	24	Elterwater	do do
	25	Kirkstone Green	Kirkstone Pass
	26	Buttermere	Honister

Table 5   *Granite quarries still operating*

County	Building Stone		Location
Cornwall	1	Bosahan	Constantine
	2	Clywoon	do
	3	De Lank	St Breward
	4	Hantergantick	do
	5	Tranack	Mabe
	6	Trevone	do
	7	Trenoweth	do
	8	Trolvis	Longdowns
Devon	9	Merrivale Devon Grey	Merrivale
Gwynedd	10	Arenig	Arenig
	11	Trevor	Trevor
Cumbria	12	Shap	Shap

Bibliography

Geology

Trueman, A.E. *Geology and Scenery in England and Wales*; Penguin, Hammondsworth.

Howe, J. Allen *The Geology of Building Stone*; Arnold, 1910.

Watson, J. *British and Foreign Building Stones*; Cambridge University Press, 1911.

Warnes, A.R. *Building Stones, their Properties, Decay and Preservation*; Benn, 1926.

Purcell, Donovan *The Stones of Ely Cathedral*; Friends of Ely Cathedral.

Practice

Greenwell, A. and Elsdon, J.V. *Practical Stone Quarrying*; Crosby, Lockwood & Son, 1913.

Knoop D. and Jones G.P. *The Medieval Mason*; Manchester University Press, 1949.

Andrews F.B. *The Mediaeval Builder and his Methods*; Oxford University Press.

General and Historical

Salzman, L.F. *Building in England down to 1540*; Oxford University Press.

Davey, Norman *A History of Building Materials*; Pheonix House, 1961.

Bedford Square Press/National Council of Social Service

Maps for the local historian
J.B. Harley
A guide to British sources, with 10 maps and 8 plates
86 pages   *90p/£1.00 by post*

Historian's guide to ordnance survey maps
J.B. Harley and C.W. Phillips
Material largely reprinted from *The Local Historian*
51 pages   *85p/95p by post*

How to read a coat of arms
Peter G. Summers
Illustrated with 30 lines drawings by Anthony Griffiths
24 pages   *50p/60p by post*

Landscapes and documents
Alan Rogers and Trevor Rowley (eds)
Contributions by seven specialists in archaeology and local history, illustrated with
maps and photographs
85 pages   *£1.50/£1.65 by post*

Logic of open field systems
Rex C. Russell
Examples from 47 Lincolnshire parishes before enclosure, illustrated with 15 maps
                                                            90p/£1.00 by post

Hedges and local history
Max D. Hooper, W.G. Hoskins, A.D. Bradshaw and D.E. Allen
Findings of a joint conference of the Standing Conference for Local History and
the Botanical Society of the British Isles
36 pages   illustrated   *75p/85p by post*

Local history and folklore
Charles Phythian-Adams
A new framework for the study of social customs by the folklorist and the historian
40 pages   85p/*95p by post*

From bookshops or by post from:
RPS Ltd Victoria Hall East Greenwich London SE10 0RF

The Local Historian

Journal of the Standing Conference for Local History

Editor: DAVID DYMOND
Staff Tutor, University of Cambridge

Information on methods of research — source material — background for further study — *The Local Historian* is the only journal in this field.

Subjects covered include sources for urban history, agricultural history, folklore of industry, English place-names, Welsh topographical literature, parish registers, Scottish local history, use of directories and census returns, computer analysis of workhouse records, and many other topics of interest to layman and scholar alike.

Book reviews and summaries of recent publications. Readers' letters

64 pages   40p   annual postal subscription £1.50.
Subscription enquiries to:
National Council of Social Service, 26 Bedford Square, London WC1.

Bath England Travel Guide 2023

Your Insider's Pocket Guide to the Best
Attractions, Hidden Gems,
Recommendations, Iconic Landmarks,
and Authentic Experiences in Bath with
detailed itineraries

Charles J. Norris

Table of Contents

160

1. Introduction

A Journey Through Time and Beauty

In the heart of England, nestled amidst rolling hills and lush countryside, lies a city that exudes an air of timeless elegance and unrivaled beauty. Welcome to Bath, a place where history comes alive, where every cobblestone street whispers tales of the past, and where the allure of Georgian architecture and Roman heritage intertwine in perfect harmony.

Picture yourself strolling through the charming streets of Bath, the gentle melody of laughter and conversation filling the air as you pass by quaint shops and inviting cafes. The honey-colored buildings stand tall, their ornate facades reflecting the golden glow of the setting sun. It is a city that captures the imagination, where every corner holds a story waiting to be discovered.

And so, dear traveler, it is with great excitement and anticipation that we present to you the "Bath England Travel Guide 2023: Your Insider's Pocket Guide to the Best Attractions, Hidden Gems, Recommendations, Iconic Landmarks, and Authentic Experiences in Bath with detailed itineraries." Within the pages of this guide, you will embark on a remarkable journey through time and beauty, unlocking the secrets of this enchanting city.

Let us begin our adventure by stepping back in time to an era when Bath was known as Aquae Sulis, a thriving Roman spa town. Imagine yourself standing at the edge of the Great Bath, the warm steam rising, and the sound of trickling water echoing in your ears. Here, two thousand years of history come alive as you delve into the mysteries of the Roman Baths, marveling at the ingenuity of the ancient engineers and immersing yourself in the stories of those who sought healing and relaxation in these sacred waters.

As we wander through the city, we find ourselves in the presence of architectural wonders that have captivated visitors for centuries. The Royal Crescent stands majestically before us, a sweeping arc of grand townhouses that epitomize Georgian elegance. Each step brings us closer to the heart of Bath's history, from the striking Bath Abbey, its intricate stained glass windows casting colorful patterns on the stone floor, to the iconic Pulteney Bridge, with its graceful arches spanning the River Avon.

But Bath is more than just a collection of remarkable landmarks; it is a city that embraces its cultural heritage and offers a wealth of authentic experiences. Step into the Jane Austen Centre and be transported to the world of the beloved author, where the romance and drama of her novels come to life. Taste the delectable flavors of Bath's culinary delights, from the fluffy and buttery Sally Lunn bun to the rich and creamy Bath Blue cheese. And don't miss the chance to browse the bustling Bath Farmers Market, where local producers showcase their finest goods, offering a taste of the region's bountiful harvest.

Within the pages of this guide, you will find carefully crafted itineraries that cater to every traveler's desire. Whether you have a day or a week to spend in Bath, we have curated a selection of experiences that will allow you to make the most of your time. Follow our recommendations to explore the city's hidden gems, unwind in its tranquil parks and gardens, and immerse yourself in the vibrant cultural scene that Bath has to offer.

Our aim is to ensure that your journey through Bath is not merely a visit, but an unforgettable experience that lingers in your heart and mind long after you have bid farewell to its picturesque streets. With insider tips, practical advice, and engaging stories, this guide is your key to unlocking the true essence of Bath.

So, dear traveler, as you turn the page and embark on this adventure with us, let the magic of Bath weave its spell upon you. Allow yourself to be transported through time, to wander through streets steep

ed in history, and to be captivated by the city's undeniable charm. Welcome to Bath, where every moment is an invitation to create memories that will stay with you forever.

1.1 About Bath

Bath is a beautiful city in the south of England, known for its Roman baths, Georgian architecture, and Jane Austen connections. It is a popular tourist destination, with attractions including the Roman Baths, the Jane Austen Centre, and the Holburne Museum.

History

The history of Bath can be traced back to the Roman era, when it was a spa town known as Aquae Sulis. The Romans built a series of baths and temples around the hot springs, which were believed to have healing properties. The baths were used by people from all over the Roman Empire, and Bath became a major center of trade and culture.

After the fall of the Roman Empire, Bath fell into decline. However, it was rediscovered in the 17th century, and the city began to grow again. In the 18th century, Bath became a fashionable spa town, and many Georgian buildings were built in the city. Bath reached its peak of popularity in the 19th century, when it was a popular destination for the wealthy and the famous.

Attractions

The Roman Baths are the most popular attraction in Bath. The baths were built in the 1st century AD, and they are still in use today. Visitors can take a tour of the baths, see the hot springs, and learn about the history of the site.

The Jane Austen Centre is another popular attraction in Bath. The centre is dedicated to the life and work of Jane Austen, who lived in Bath for a time. The centre has exhibits on Austen's life, her books, and the Regency period.

The Holburne Museum is a fine art museum in Bath. The museum has a collection of paintings, sculptures, and decorative arts from the 17th to the 20th centuries.

Activities

There are many things to do in Bath besides visiting the attractions. Visitors can take a stroll through the city's Georgian streets, shop in the boutiques, or have a picnic in the Royal Crescent Gardens. Bath is also a great place to relax and enjoy the spa treatments.

Accommodation

There are many hotels, bed and breakfasts, and guesthouses in Bath. The city also has a number of self-catering apartments and holiday cottages.

Getting there

Bath is well-connected by train, bus, and car. The nearest airports are Bristol Airport and Heathrow Airport.

Bath is a beautiful and historic city with a lot to offer visitors. Whether you are interested in history, culture, or simply want to relax and enjoy the spa treatments, Bath is a great place to visit.

Bath is a great place to visit for a weekend getaway or a longer vacation. There is something for everyone in this charming city.

2. Planning Your Trip

2.1 Best Time to Visit Bath

Bath is a popular tourist destination, and the best time to visit is during the spring or fall when the weather is mild and there are fewer crowds.

Spring

Spring is a great time to visit Bath. The weather is usually mild, with average temperatures ranging from 50 to 70 degrees Fahrenheit. The city is in bloom, with flowers in the parks and gardens. There are also a number of festivals held in Bath during the spring, including the Bath Flower Show and the Bath Literature Festival.

Things to do in Bath during spring

Visit the Roman Baths: The Roman Baths are one of the most popular attractions in Bath. They were built in the first century AD and are still in use today. You can take a tour of the baths and learn about their history.

Explore the Georgian architecture: Bath is home to some of the finest Georgian architecture in the world. Take a walk around the city and admire the beautiful buildings.

Enjoy the spa treatments: Bath is famous for its spa treatments. There are a number of spas in the city where you can relax and enjoy a variety of treatments.

Attend a festival: There are a number of festivals held in Bath during the spring. The Bath Flower Show is a great place to see flowers from all over the world. The Bath Literature Festival features a variety of authors and speakers.

Fall

Fall is another great time to visit Bath. The weather is usually mild, with average temperatures ranging from 40 to 60 degrees Fahrenheit. The leaves change color, and the city is a beautiful sight to see.

Things to do in Bath during fall

Visit the Royal Crescent: The Royal Crescent is a row of 30 Georgian townhouses. It is one of the most iconic landmarks in Bath.

Visit the Circus: The Circus is a circular Georgian street. It is another iconic landmark in Bath.

Take a walk along the River Avon: The River Avon runs through Bath. It is a great place to take a walk or a boat ride.

Visit the Jane Austen Centre: The Jane Austen Centre is a museum dedicated to the life and work of Jane Austen. Austen lived in Bath for a time, and the museum is located in her former home.

Winter

Winter is the least popular time to visit Bath, but it can be a magical time to visit. The city is decorated for Christmas, and there are a number of festive events held.

Things to do in Bath during winter

Visit the Christmas market: The Christmas market is held in the city center every year. It is a great place to buy Christmas gifts and food.

See a Christmas concert: There are a number of Christmas concerts held in Bath every year. The Bath Bach Choir is a popular choir that performs a number of Christmas concerts.

Go ice skating: There is an ice skating rink in the city center every year. It is a great place to enjoy the winter weather.

Bath is a beautiful city that can be enjoyed any time of year. The best time to visit depends on your personal preferences. If you prefer mild weather and fewer crowds, spring or fall are the best times to visit. If you enjoy festive events, winter is a great time to visit.

2.2 Getting to Bath

By car

The easiest way to get to Bath by car is to take the M4 motorway. The M4 runs from London to South Wales, and it passes just north of Bath. There are a number of car parks in Bath, and parking is usually available.

By train

Bath Spa railway station is located in the heart of the city. There are regular trains from London Paddington, Bristol Temple Meads, and other major cities. The journey time from London is around 1 hour and 30 minutes.

By bus

National Express buses run from London Victoria Coach Station to Bath. The journey time is around 2 hours. There are also a number of local bus services that connect Bath with other towns and villages in the area.

By plane

The nearest airport to Bath is Bristol Airport. There are regular flights from London Heathrow, Gatwick, and other major airports. The journey time from London is around 1 hour. From Bristol Airport, you can take a taxi, bus, or train to Bath.

Once you arrive in Bath, you can explore the city on foot or by bike. There are also a number of hop-on, hop-off buses that run around the city.

2.3 Getting Around Bath

Bath is a small city, so it's easy to get around on foot or by bike. However, there are also public transportation options available if you prefer not to walk or bike.

By Foot

The best way to see Bath is by foot. The city is compact and walkable, and there are plenty of things to see and do within a short walk of any point in the city center.

Some of the most popular walking areas in Bath include:

The Royal Crescent

The Circus

The Abbey Churchyard

The Pulteney Bridge

The Parade Gardens

By Bike

Bath is also a great city to explore by bike. There are a number of bike paths and lanes throughout the city, and it's a great way to get around and see the sights without having to worry about traffic.

You can rent bikes from a number of different shops in Bath. The cost of renting a bike varies depending on the length of time you rent it for.

By Public Transportation

If you don't want to walk or bike, there are also a number of public transportation options available in Bath.

Buses: First Bus is the primary bus operator in Bath. Buses run throughout the city and to nearby towns and villages.

Trains: Bath Spa railway station is located in the city center. Trains run to London, Bristol, and other major cities in the UK.

Park and Ride: There arc four Park and Ride facilities located on the outskirts of Bath. These facilities allow you to park your car and then take a bus into the city center.

Taxis

Taxis are also available in Bath. Taxis can be hailed on the street or booked in advance.

Car Rental

If you're planning on doing a lot of exploring outside of Bath, you may want to consider renting a car. There are a number of car rental companies located in Bath.

Tips for Getting Around Bath

If you're planning on doing a lot of walking, be sure to wear comfortable shoes.

Bath can be a busy city, so be sure to be aware of your surroundings when walking or biking.

If you're planning on taking public transportation, be sure to purchase a ticket in advance.

Bath is a great city to explore, so be sure to take your time and enjoy your visit.

2.4 Where to Stay in Bath

Choosing the perfect place to stay is an integral part of planning your visit to Bath. The city offers a diverse range of accommodations that cater to every taste and budget. Whether you seek a luxurious boutique hotel, a cozy bed and breakfast, or a comfortable self-catering apartment, Bath has an array of options to ensure a memorable stay. In this section, we will guide you through the different neighborhoods and highlight some of the top accommodations in each area, allowing you to find the ideal home away from home during your time in Bath.

1. City Center: Where History Meets Convenience

The City Center is the beating heart of Bath, where history and modernity coexist in perfect harmony. Staying in this vibrant neighborhood places you within walking distance of the city's major attractions, shops, and restaurants. Here are some top accommodation options in the City Center:

- The Royal Crescent Hotel & Spa: Experience luxury and elegance at this iconic hotel located in the renowned Royal Crescent. Indulge in spacious rooms, impeccable service, and a tranquil spa that will transport you to a world of relaxation.

- The Gainsborough Bath Spa: Immerse yourself in the ultimate pampering experience at this five-star hotel that boasts its own thermal waters. Unwind in luxurious rooms, rejuvenate in the spa, and savor exquisite dining options.

- The Francis Hotel: This historic Georgian townhouse turned boutique hotel offers a blend of classic charm and modern comfort. With stylish rooms, a cozy lounge, and a central location, it is the perfect base for exploring Bath.

2. Bathwick: Tranquility by the River

Located just east of the City Center, Bathwick offers a peaceful retreat away from the bustling crowds. Its proximity to the River Avon and beautiful green spaces makes it a popular choice for those seeking tranquility. Here are some notable accommodations in Bathwick:

- The Bath Priory: Indulge in luxury and seclusion at this elegant country house hotel. Surrounded by beautiful gardens, it offers spacious rooms, a Michelin-starred restaurant, and a serene spa for an unforgettable stay.

- The Kennard: Step into this charming Georgian townhouse that exudes warmth and character. With individually decorated rooms, friendly service, and a delightful garden, The Kennard offers a cozy and intimate experience.

3. Widcombe: Charm and Convenience

Situated on the southern banks of the River Avon, Widcombe combines charm and convenience with its proximity to the City Center. This residential area offers a range of accommodations for those seeking a quieter atmosphere. Consider the following options in Widcombe:

- The Windsor: Stay in this elegant guesthouse that offers comfortable rooms, friendly service, and a delicious breakfast. With its convenient location near the train station and a short walk to the City Center, it is a popular choice among travelers.

- The Bear: This historic inn, dating back to the 18th century, provides a cozy and traditional English experience. With its charming rooms, pub-style restaurant, and friendly ambiance, The Bear is a delightful place to call home during your stay in Bath.

4. Larkhall: A Quaint Village Atmosphere

Located northeast of the City Center, Larkhall offers a village-like atmosphere and a range of local amenities. It provides a quieter setting while still being within easy reach of Bath's attractions. Consider these accommodations in Larkhall:

- Brooks Guesthouse: Enjoy the comforts of home at this boutique guesthouse with its stylish rooms and welcoming atmosphere. With a cozy lounge and garden, it offers a relaxed and friendly environment for your stay.

- Harington's City Hotel: Experience a blend of historic charm and modern comfort at this boutique hotel. With its individually decorated rooms, attentive service, and central location, Harington's City Hotel provides a memorable stay.

5. Outside the City: Rural Retreats and Beyond

For those seeking a countryside escape or a base to explore the wider region, there are excellent accommodations available just outside the city limits of Bath. Here are a couple of options for your consideration:

- The Pig near Bath: Situated in the idyllic Mendip Hills, this country house hotel offers rustic luxury and stunning views. With its focus on locally sourced cuisine and a tranquil setting, it provides a unique and unforgettable stay.

- Lucknam Park: Indulge in luxury and elegance at this grand country estate located a short drive from Bath. Set in a sprawling parkland, it offers exquisite rooms, fine dining, an award-winning spa, and a range of outdoor activities.

Now that you have a glimpse of the various neighborhoods and accommodations Bath has to offer, it's time to make your choice. Consider your preferences, budget, and desired location, and select the perfect place to rest and rejuvenate after your days of exploration in this remarkable city. No matter where you choose to stay, Bath's warm hospitality and timeless beauty will make your visit an experience to treasure.

2.5 Essential Travel Tips

1. Book your accommodation in advance. Bath is a popular tourist destination, so it's important to book your accommodation in advance, especially if you're traveling during the summer months.

2. Get a Bath City Card. The Bath City Card gives you free entry to many of Bath's attractions, including the Roman Baths, the Holburne Museum, and the Jane Austen Centre. It also offers discounts on other activities and attractions in the city.

3. Explore the Roman Baths. The Roman Baths are one of the most popular tourist attractions in Bath. You can take a tour of the baths, learn about the history of the site, and even take a dip in the thermal waters.

4. Visit the Jane Austen Centre. The Jane Austen Centre is a museum dedicated to the life and work of Jane Austen, who lived in Bath for a time. You can see exhibits on Austen's life, her writing, and her influence on popular culture.

5. Take a walk along the River Avon. The River Avon runs through the heart of Bath, and it's a great place to take a walk, have a picnic, or rent a boat.

6. Visit the Holburne Museum. The Holburne Museum is a fine art museum that houses a collection of paintings, sculptures, and decorative arts.

7. Go shopping in Bath. Bath is a great place to go shopping. You'll find a wide variety of shops, from high-end boutiques to independent stores.

8. Enjoy the nightlife in Bath. Bath has a lively nightlife scene. There are bars, clubs, and restaurants open late into the night.

9. Take a day trip to Stonehenge. Stonehenge is a prehistoric monument located about 10 miles from Bath. It's a UNESCO World Heritage Site and one of the most popular tourist attractions in England.

10. Visit the Roman city of Aquae Sulis. Aquae Sulis was the Roman town that Bath was built on. You can visit the ruins of the town, including the baths, temples, and amphitheater.

11. Go for a hike in the countryside around Bath. There are many beautiful hiking trails in the countryside around Bath. You can take a walk through the woods, along the river, or up to the top of a hill for stunning views of the city.

12. Visit the Bath Royal Crescent. The Bath Royal Crescent is a row of 30 Georgian townhouses that were built in the 18th century. It's a UNESCO World Heritage Site and one of the most iconic landmarks in Bath.

13. Take a ride on the Bath Skyline Gondola. The Bath Skyline Gondola offers stunning views of Bath from above. The gondolas travel up and down a 1,000-foot-long cableway that runs between the city center and the top of a hill.

14. Attend a concert or performance in Bath. Bath is a vibrant city with a thriving arts scene. There are always concerts, plays, and musicals happening in the city.

15. Have a spa treatment. Bath is known for its thermal waters, and there are many spas in the city that offer a variety of treatments.

16. Eat at a traditional English pub. Bath has many traditional English pubs where you can enjoy a pint of beer and a hearty meal.

17. Learn about Bath's history. Bath has a long and fascinating history. There are many museums and historical sites in the city where you can learn about the city's past.

18. Take a cooking class. Bath is home to a number of cooking schools where you can learn how to make traditional English dishes.

19. Join a walking tour. There are many walking tours of Bath that offer a unique perspective on the city.

20. Just relax and enjoy yourself. Bath is a beautiful city with a lot to offer visitors. Take some time to relax, explore, and enjoy your stay.

3. Exploring Bath: An Overview

3.1 Top Attractions at a Glance

Here are some of the top attractions in Bath:

The Roman Baths: The Roman Baths are the most famous attraction in Bath. They are a UNESCO World Heritage Site and have been in use for over 2,000 years. The baths are open to the public and offer guided tours.

The Abbey Church of St. Peter and St. Paul: The Abbey Church is a beautiful example of Georgian architecture. It was built in the 18th century and is a popular place for weddings and concerts.

The Royal Crescent: The Royal Crescent is a row of 30 Georgian townhouses that is considered to be one of the finest examples of Georgian architecture in the world. The houses are now owned by private residents, but they can be viewed from the street.

Pulteney Bridge: Pulteney Bridge is a beautiful bridge that crosses the River Avon. It was built in the 18th century and is modeled after the Ponte Vecchio in Florence.

The Jane Austen Centre: The Jane Austen Centre is a museum dedicated to the life and work of Jane Austen. The museum is located in a Georgian townhouse that is believed to have been used as a model for some of Austen's novels.

Bath Skyline Walk: The Bath Skyline Walk is a popular walking path that offers stunning views of the city. The walk starts at the top of Pulteney Bridge and winds its way up through the hills to the Royal Crescent.

Bath Christmas Market: The Bath Christmas Market is a popular event that takes place every year in December. The market features over 100 stalls selling food, drink, and Christmas gifts.

3.2 Bath's Neighborhoods

The city is also home to a number of interesting neighborhoods, each with its own unique character.

The City Center

The city center is the heart of Bath, and it's where you'll find most of the major attractions, including the Roman baths, the Pump Room, and the Assembly Rooms. The city center is also home to a number of shops, restaurants, and bars.

The Royal Crescent

The Royal Crescent is one of the most iconic landmarks in Bath, and it's a UNESCO World Heritage Site. The crescent is a row of 30 Grade I listed Georgian townhouses, and it's one of the most photographed places in the city.

The Circus

The Circus is another iconic landmark in Bath, and it's located just across from the Royal Crescent. The Circus is a circular Georgian piazza, and it's surrounded by 33 Grade I listed townhouses.

Bathwick

Bathwick is a neighborhood located to the west of the city center. Bathwick is home to a number of

Georgian townhouses, as well as the Jane Austen Centre, which is dedicated to the life and work of the famous author.

Hanover Buildings

Hanover Buildings is a Georgian terrace located to the north of the city center. Hanover Buildings is home to a number of shops, restaurants, and bars, and it's a popular spot for locals and visitors alike.

The Southgate

The Southgate is a Georgian gateway located to the south of the city center. The Southgate is a popular spot for walkers and cyclists, and it offers stunning views of the city.

Bathwick Hill

Bathwick Hill is a steep hill located to the west of the city center. Bathwick Hill is home to a number of Georgian townhouses, as well as the Prior Park Landscape Garden, which is a UNESCO World Heritage Site.

The Old Town

The Old Town is the oldest part of Bath, and it's home to a number of historic buildings, including the Bath Abbey, the Guildhall, and the Roman Baths Museum. The Old Town is also a great place to find traditional Bath shops, restaurants, and pubs.

Bathwick Village

Bathwick Village is a small village located to the west of the city center. Bathwick Village is home to a number of Georgian townhouses, as well as the Batheaston Priory, which is a Grade I listed building.

These are just a few of the many neighborhoods in Bath. Each neighborhood has its own unique character, and there's something for everyone to enjoy. So whether you're interested in history, architecture, shopping, or dining, you're sure to find something to love in Bath.

3.3 Local Customs and Etiquette

If you are planning a trip to Bath, it is important to be aware of some of the local customs and etiquette.

Here are a few tips to help you make the most of your visit:

Be aware of the dress code. Bath is a relatively formal city, and it is important to dress appropriately when visiting certain places, such as the Roman baths or the Jane Austen Centre. For men, this means wearing a jacket and tie, and for women, it means wearing a dress or skirt and blouse.

Be respectful of the local culture. Bath is a historic city with a rich culture, and it is important to be respectful of this when visiting. This means avoiding loud behavior, littering, and taking photographs without permission.

Be aware of the local customs. Bath is a very welcoming city, but there are a few customs that you should be aware of. For example, it is customary to say "hello" and "goodbye" when entering and leaving a shop or restaurant. It is also customary to tip your server in restaurants.

 Be prepared for the weather. Bath can be a very wet city, so it is important to be prepared for the weather. This means packing an umbrella and waterproof jacket.

Following these tips will help you make the most of your visit to Bath. With its rich history, beautiful architecture, and vibrant culture, Bath is a city that is sure to amaze and delight.

3.4 Currency, Language, and Safety Information

Currency

The currency in Bath is the British pound (GBP). The exchange rate is currently around £1 = $1.30. There are many banks and currency exchange bureaus in Bath where you can exchange your currency.

Language

The official language in Bath is English. However, many people in Bath also speak French, German, and Spanish. If you are not fluent in English, you should be able to get by with a little bit of French or German.

Safety Information

Bath is a very safe city. However, there are a few things you should keep in mind to stay safe:

 Be aware of your surroundings and do not walk alone at night.

Do not leave valuables unattended.

Be careful when crossing the street.

Be aware of pickpockets in crowded areas.

4. Must-Visit Attractions in Bath

4.1 The Roman Baths

The Roman Baths are one of the most popular tourist attractions in Bath, England. The baths were built by the Romans in the 1st century AD, and they were used for bathing and socializing for over 400 years. The baths are now a UNESCO World Heritage Site, and they offer visitors a fascinating glimpse into Roman life.

The baths are located in the heart of Bath, and they are surrounded by beautiful Georgian architecture. The entrance to the baths is through the Roman Baths Museum, which houses a collection of Roman artifacts found at the site. The museum also has a theater that shows a short film about the history of the baths.

From the museum, visitors enter the Great Bath, which is the largest of the baths. The Great Bath is a large, rectangular pool that is filled with hot spring water. The water in the Great Bath is said to have healing properties, and it was used by the Romans for bathing, swimming, and socializing.

The Roman Baths also include a number of other smaller baths, as well as a sauna and a steam room. The baths are open to the public year-round, and they offer a variety of tours and activities.

Here are some of the things you can see and do at the Roman Baths:

Visit the Roman Baths Museum: The museum houses a collection of Roman artifacts found at the site, including coins, jewelry, and pottery. The museum also has a theater that shows a short film about the history of the baths.

Explore the baths: The baths are open to the public year-round, and they offer a variety of tours and activities. You can take a guided tour of the baths, or you can explore them on your own.

Relax in the spa: Thermae Bath Spa is a modern spa that is built on the site of the Roman baths. The spa offers a variety of treatments, including bathing in the hot spring water.

Enjoy the city of Bath: Bath is a beautiful city with a lot to offer visitors. There are a number of historical buildings to see, as well as shops, restaurants, and bars.

Here are some tips for visiting the Roman Baths:

The Roman Baths are a popular tourist attraction, so it is recommended to book your tickets in advance.

The baths can get crowded, so it is a good idea to visit early in the morning or later in the afternoon.

There is a lot to see at the Roman Baths, so it is a good idea to allow at least a few hours to explore the site.

The Roman Baths are wheelchair accessible, and there are a number of accessible facilities available.

The Roman Baths are open year-round, but they are busiest during the summer months.

The Roman Baths are a fascinating place to visit, and they offer a unique glimpse into Roman life. If you are planning a trip to Bath, be sure to add the Roman Baths to your itinerary.

4.2 Bath Abbey

Bath Abbey is a beautiful and historic church located in the heart of Bath, England. It is one of the most popular tourist attractions in the city, and for good reason. The abbey is a stunning example of Gothic architecture, and it is full of history and interesting features.

History

Bath Abbey was founded in the 7th century by King Ine of Wessex. The original church was made of wood, but it was rebuilt in stone in the 11th century. The abbey was later dissolved by Henry VIII in the 16th century, but it was restored in the 18th century.

Architecture

Bath Abbey is a beautiful example of Gothic architecture. The exterior of the abbey is made of Bath stone, which gives it a distinctive yellow color. The interior of the abbey is even more impressive. The nave is incredibly tall, and the ceiling is covered in intricate fan vaulting. The abbey also contains a number of beautiful stained glass windows and other works of art.

Features

Bath Abbey is full of interesting features. One of the most popular features is the Whispering Gallery. This is a narrow gallery that runs around the inside of the abbey dome. If you stand at one end of the gallery and whisper, your voice can be heard clearly by someone standing at the other end.

Another popular feature is the Cosmati pavement. This is a beautiful mosaic floor that was created in the 13th century. The pavement is made up of small pieces of colored marble, and it is decorated with intricate patterns.

Tours

Bath Abbey offers a number of tours that allow visitors to learn more about the abbey's history and architecture. There are also a number of special events that take place at the abbey throughout the year, such as concerts and organ recitals.

Getting there

Bath Abbey is located in the heart of Bath, England. It is a short walk from the train station and the bus station. The abbey is also open to the public for free.

Conclusion

Bath Abbey is a beautiful and historic church that is well worth a visit. It is a great place to learn about Bath's history and architecture, and it is also a great place to simply relax and enjoy the peace and quiet.

Additional Information

Here is some additional information about Bath Abbey:

The abbey is open to the public from 9am to 5pm, 7 days a week.

There is no admission charge to visit the abbey.

Guided tours are available for a small fee.

Bath Abbey is a popular wedding venue.

The abbey is also a popular concert venue.

Bath Abbey is a Grade I listed building, which means that it is considered to be of special architectural or historic interest.

Tips for Visiting

Here are some tips for visiting Bath Abbey:

If you are planning to visit the abbey during the summer months, it is advisable to book your tickets in advance.

If you are visiting the abbey with children, be sure to check out the abbey's website for information on family-friendly activities.

Be sure to dress appropriately for a church service.

Be respectful of the abbey's religious significance.

Take your time and enjoy the beauty of the abbey.

4.3 The Royal Crescent

The Royal Crescent is one of the most iconic landmarks in Bath, England. It is a row of 30 terraced houses laid out in a sweeping crescent, and is considered to be one of the finest examples of Georgian architecture in the world. The houses were designed by John Wood the Younger, and were built between 1767 and 1774.

The Royal Crescent is located in the heart of Bath, on the south side of the River Avon. It is a short walk from the Roman Baths and the Pulteney Bridge. The crescent is set in its own parkland, and offers stunning views of the city and the surrounding countryside.

The houses in the Royal Crescent are all Grade I listed buildings, which means that they are of special architectural or historic interest. They are all privately owned, and many of them are still occupied by families. However, a few of the houses have been converted into hotels or museums.

No. 1 Royal Crescent is a museum that tells the story of the Royal Crescent and its residents. The house has been restored to its Georgian appearance, and visitors can see how the wealthy people of Bath lived in the 18th century. The museum also has a number of exhibits on the history of Bath and its architecture.

The Royal Crescent is a popular tourist destination, and it is often crowded with visitors. However, it is still possible to enjoy the beauty of the crescent and its surroundings. The best time to visit is early in the morning or late in the evening, when the crowds have thinned out.

Here are some of the things you can do when visiting The Royal Crescent:

Take a walk along the crescent and admire the architecture.

Visit No. 1 Royal Crescent museum and learn about the history of the crescent and its residents.

Enjoy the views of the city and the surrounding countryside from the parkland.

Have a picnic lunch in the parkland.

Take a boat trip on the River Avon and see the Royal Crescent from a different perspective.

The Royal Crescent is a beautiful and historic landmark that is well worth a visit. It is a great place to learn about the history of Bath and to enjoy the beauty of Georgian architecture.

4.4 Pulteney Bridge

Pulteney Bridge is a renowned landmark in Bath, England, and is listed as a Grade I building. It is one of only four bridges in the world to have shops on both sides of its entire span. Robert Adam designed the bridge and it was finished in 1774. It was named after Frances Pulteney, the wife of William Johnstone Pulteney, who was a wealthy landowner and politician.

Pulteney Bridge is a beautiful example of Georgian architecture. It is made of Bath stone and has a Palladian style. The bridge is 300 feet long and 20 feet wide. It has five arches and is supported by 13 piers.

The shops on Pulteney Bridge are a mix of independent boutiques and high-street stores. There are also a number of cafes and restaurants on the bridge. The bridge is a popular tourist destination and is a great place to take a stroll, do some shopping, or enjoy a meal.

In addition to its beauty and historical significance, Pulteney Bridge is also a popular spot for photography. The bridge is often used as a backdrop for wedding photos and other special events.

If you are planning a visit to Bath, be sure to include Pulteney Bridge on your list of must-see attractions. It is a beautiful and historic bridge that is sure to impress.

Here are some of the things you can do at Pulteney Bridge:

Walk across the bridge and admire the views of the River Avon and the city of Bath.

Browse the shops on the bridge and find some unique souvenirs or gifts.

Enjoy a meal at one of the cafes or restaurants on the bridge.

Take a photo of the bridge from the riverbank or from the top of the bridge.

Visit the Pump Room, which is located just off the bridge.

Take a tour of the Roman baths, which are located nearby.

Explore the other attractions in Bath, such as the Assembly Rooms, the Royal Crescent, and the Jane Austen Centre.

Pulteney Bridge is a beautiful and historic bridge that is sure to impress visitors to Bath. It is a great place to take a stroll, do some shopping, or enjoy a meal. Be sure to include it on your list of must-see attractions when you visit Bath.

4.5 The Jane Austen Centre

The Jane Austen Centre is a museum and tourist attraction in Bath, England, dedicated to the life and works of Jane Austen. The Centre is located in a Georgian townhouse in the heart of the city, and it offers a variety of exhibits and activities that explore Austen's life, her writing, and the Regency period in which she lived.

The Centre's permanent exhibition tells the story of Austen's life through a series of interactive displays. Visitors can learn about Austen's family, her education, her social circle, and her writing process. The exhibition also features a number of Austen's letters, manuscripts, and other personal belongings.

In addition to the permanent exhibition, the Jane Austen Centre also offers a variety of temporary exhibitions, events, and workshops. These events are designed to appeal to a wide range of visitors, from Austen enthusiasts to those who are simply curious about her life and work.

The Jane Austen Centre is a popular tourist destination, and it is well worth a visit for anyone who is interested in Austen or the Regency period. The Centre is open year-round, and it offers a variety of admission options to suit your budget.

Here are some of the things you can do at the Jane Austen Centre:

Explore the permanent exhibition: The Centre's permanent exhibition tells the story of Jane Austen's life through a series of interactive displays. Visitors can learn about Austen's family, her education, her social circle, and her writing process. The exhibition also features a number of Austen's letters, manuscripts, and other personal belongings.

Take part in a temporary exhibition, event, or workshop: The Jane Austen Centre also offers a variety of temporary exhibitions, events, and workshops. These events are designed to appeal to a wide range of visitors, from Austen enthusiasts to those who are simply curious about her life and work.

Enjoy a Regency-style tea: The Jane Austen Centre has its own Regency-style tearoom, where you can enjoy a traditional afternoon tea. The tearoom is located in the basement of the Centre, and it is decorated in a traditional Regency style.

Take a guided tour: The Jane Austen Centre offers a variety of guided tours, which are a great way to learn more about Austen and the Regency period. Tours are available for individuals and groups, and they can be tailored to your interests.

Shop for souvenirs: The Jane Austen Centre has a gift shop, where you can buy souvenirs, books, and other Austen-related items.

The Jane Austen Centre is a great place to learn more about Jane Austen and the Regency period. The Centre is well-organized and informative, and it offers a variety of activities and events to appeal to a wide range of visitors. If you are planning a trip to Bath, be sure to add the Jane Austen Centre to your itinerary.

4.6 Thermae Bath Spa

Thermae Bath Spa is a world-class spa located in the heart of Bath, England. It is built on the site of the original Roman baths, and uses the same natural hot springs to provide its guests with a unique and luxurious experience.

The spa offers a variety of different facilities, including indoor and outdoor pools, steam rooms, saunas, and treatment rooms. There is also a restaurant and bar, where guests can enjoy a delicious meal or drink while relaxing in the spa's tranquil surroundings.

Thermae Bath Spa is the perfect place to relax and unwind after a long day of sightseeing. It is also a great place to celebrate a special occasion, or to simply treat yourself to some well-deserved pampering.

Here is a more detailed look at some of the things you can do at Thermae Bath Spa:

Soak in the thermal pools: Thermae Bath Spa has two thermal pools, one indoor and one outdoor. The indoor pool is heated to a temperature of 33 degrees Celsius, while the outdoor pool is heated to a temperature of 36 degrees Celsius. Both pools are filled with mineral-rich water from the same hot springs that were used by the Romans over 2,000 years ago.

Experience the steam rooms and saunas: Thermae Bath Spa has four steam rooms and two saunas. The steam rooms are heated to a temperature of 45 degrees Celsius, while the saunas are heated to a temperature of 85 degrees Celsius. The steam rooms and saunas are a great way to relax and detoxify your body.

Get a treatment: Thermae Bath Spa offers a variety of different treatments, including massages, facials, and body wraps. The treatments are all designed to help you relax, rejuvenate, and improve your overall health and well-being.

Enjoy a meal or drink: Thermae Bath Spa has a restaurant and bar, where guests can enjoy a delicious meal or drink while relaxing in the spa's tranquil surroundings. The restaurant serves a variety of different dishes, including fresh seafood, locally-sourced meat and vegetables, and traditional English fare. The bar offers a wide selection of wines, beers, and cocktails.

In addition to the facilities mentioned above, Thermae Bath Spa also offers a variety of other activities, such as yoga classes, Pilates classes, and guided meditation sessions. These activities are a great way to add an extra element of relaxation and wellness to your spa experience.

Thermae Bath Spa is a truly unique and luxurious spa experience. It is the perfect place to relax, unwind, and pamper yourself. If you are looking for a truly special place to visit in Bath, then Thermae Bath Spa is definitely worth considering.

Here are some additional tips for planning your visit to Thermae Bath Spa:

Book your tickets in advance: Thermae Bath Spa is a popular tourist destination, so it is advisable to book your tickets in advance, especially if you are planning to visit during peak season.

Wear comfortable clothing: You will be spending a lot of time in the pools and steam rooms, so it is advisable to wear comfortable clothing that you don't mind getting wet.

Bring a towel: Thermae Bath Spa does not provide towels, so you will need to bring your own.

Arrive early: The spa can get quite busy, so it is advisable to arrive early to avoid long queues.

Take your time: There is no need to rush at Thermae Bath Spa. Take your time and relax in the pools, steam rooms, and saunas.

Enjoy yourself: Thermae Bath Spa is a truly unique and luxurious experience. Relax, unwind, and pamper yourself.

5. Hidden Gems in Bath

5.1 Prior Park Landscape Garden

If you're looking for a hidden gem, look no further than Prior Park Landscape Garden, located just south of Bath, Somerset, England. This 18th century garden was designed by the poet Alexander Pope and the landscape gardener Capability Brown, and is now owned by the National Trust. It was influential in defining the style known as the "English landscape garden" in continental Europe, and is listed as Grade I in the Register of Historic Parks and Gardens of special historic interest in England.

History

Prior Park was originally a monastic estate, but it was abandoned in the 16th century. In the 1720s, the local entrepreneur and philanthropist Ralph Allen purchased the estate and began to transform it into a country estate. He commissioned Pope and Brown to design the landscape garden, and construction began in 1734. The garden was completed in 1764, shortly after Allen's death.

Features

The Prior Park Landscape Garden is a beautiful example of an English landscape garden. It features winding paths, hidden features, and stunning views over Bath. The garden is home to a variety of trees, shrubs, and flowers, and it is also home to a number of follies, including a Palladian bridge, a grotto, and a temple.

The Palladian Bridge

The Palladian Bridge is one of the most iconic features of Prior Park Landscape Garden. It is a 100-foot-long bridge that crosses a lake in the center of the garden. The bridge was designed by Capability Brown and is inspired by the work of the Italian architect Andrea Palladio.

The Grotto

The Grotto is a hidden cave located in the garden. It is decorated with shells, fossils, and other natural materials. The grotto is a popular spot for visitors to relax and enjoy the peace and quiet of the garden.

The Temple

The Temple is a small, classical temple located in the garden. It was built in the 1750s and is dedicated to the goddess Diana. The temple is a popular spot for weddings and other special events.

Visit

Prior Park Landscape Garden is open to the public year-round. Admission is charged. The garden is a great place to spend a day exploring the beauty of nature and the history of Bath.

Nearby Attractions

In addition to Prior Park Landscape Garden, there are a number of other attractions nearby, including:

Bath Abbey

The Roman Baths

The Holburne Museum

The Jane Austen Centre

The Bath Skyline Walk

Getting There

Prior Park Landscape Garden is located just south of Bath. It is easily accessible by car, bus, or train.

By car: From Bath, follow the A46 towards Bristol. Turn left onto Prior Park Road and follow the signs to the garden.

By bus: Take the number 1 bus from Bath city centre to Prior Park. The bus stop is located just outside the entrance to the garden.

By train: Take the train from Bath Spa railway station to Prior Park station. The station is located a short walk from the garden.

Tips

The best time to visit Prior Park Landscape Garden is in the spring or fall, when the weather is mild and the gardens are in bloom.

Allow plenty of time to explore the garden. There is a lot to see and do, and you don't want to miss anything.

Wear comfortable shoes. There are a lot of paths to walk on, and you'll want to be comfortable.

Bring a camera. You'll want to capture the beauty of the garden for posterity.

Prior Park Landscape Garden is a hidden gem located just south of Bath. It is a beautiful example of an English landscape garden, and it is a great place to spend a day exploring the beauty of nature and the history of Bath.

5.2 Victoria Art Gallery

The Victoria Art Gallery is a hidden gem in Bath. It is a public art museum that houses a collection of paintings, sculpture, and decorative arts. The gallery was founded in 1897 and is located in the heart of Bath, on Bridge Street.

The Victoria Art Gallery has a wide variety of art on display, from the 15th century to the present day. The collection includes works by some of the most famous artists in the world, such as Van Gogh, Monet, and Picasso. The gallery also has a number of important British artists, including John Constable, J.M.W. Turner, and William Blake.

In addition to its permanent collection, the Victoria Art Gallery also hosts a number of temporary exhibitions throughout the year. These exhibitions often feature work by contemporary artists or explore a particular theme in art history.

The Victoria Art Gallery is a great place to spend a few hours exploring the world of art. It is a free museum, so there is no excuse not to visit.

Here are some of the highlights of the Victoria Art Gallery:

The Van Gogh Room: This room is home to a number of important works by Vincent van Gogh, including "Sunflowers" and "The Starry Night."

The Monet Room: This room features a number of works by Claude Monet, including "Water Lilies" and "Impression, Sunrise."

The Picasso Room: This room is home to a number of important works by Pablo Picasso, including "Guernica" and "Les Demoiselles d'Avignon."

The Constable Room: This room features a number of important works by John Constable, including "The Hay Wain" and "Salisbury Cathedral from the Meadows."

The Turner Room: This room features a number of important works by J.M.W. Turner, including "The Fighting Temeraire" and "Rain, Steam and Speed."

The Blake Room: This room features a number of important works by William Blake, including "The Great Red Dragon and the Woman Clothed in Sun" and "Songs of Innocence and Experience."

In addition to its permanent collection, the Victoria Art Gallery also hosts a number of temporary exhibitions throughout the year. These exhibitions often feature work by contemporary artists or explore a particular theme in art history.

Here are some of the upcoming exhibitions at the Victoria Art Gallery:

"The Impressionists: From Paris to Bath" (March 1-June 30, 2023): This exhibition will explore the influence of Impressionism on British art.

"The Renaissance: A Golden Age" (July 1-September 30, 2023): This exhibition will showcase some of the most important works of art from the Renaissance period.

"The British Portrait: From Holbein to Hockney" (October 1-December 31, 2023): This exhibition will explore the history of portraiture in Britain.

The Victoria Art Gallery is a great place to spend a few hours exploring the world of art. It is a free museum, so there is no excuse not to visit.

Here are some tips for visiting the Victoria Art Gallery:

The gallery is open from 10:00am to 5:00pm, Tuesday to Sunday.

The gallery is closed on Mondays and bank holidays.

Admission is free.

The gallery is wheelchair accessible.

The gallery has a cafe and a gift shop.

The Victoria Art Gallery is located in the heart of Bath, on Bridge Street.

Here are some directions to the Victoria Art Gallery:

From Bath Spa railway station: The gallery is a 10-minute walk from the station. Head south on Manvers Street and turn left onto Bridge Street. The gallery will be on your right.

From the city center: The gallery is a 5-minute walk from the Roman Baths. Head west on Queen Square and turn right onto Bridge Street. The gallery will be on your left.

I hope you enjoy your visit to the Victoria Art Gallery!

5.3 Fashion Museum Bath

The Fashion Museum Bath is a hidden gem in the city of Bath. It is located in the Assembly Rooms, a beautiful Georgian building in the heart of the city.

The museum has a collection of over 100,000 objects, including dresses, suits, shoes, and accessories from the 17th century to the present day.

The museum was founded by Doris Langley Moore, a fashion historian and collector. Moore began collecting fashion in the early 1900s, and her collection eventually grew to over 5,000 pieces. In 1963, Moore donated her collection to the city of Bath, and the Fashion Museum was opened the following year.

The Fashion Museum is divided into three main galleries:

The Georgian Gallery: This gallery showcases fashion from the 17th and 18th centuries. The exhibits include dresses, suits, and accessories from the Georgian era, as well as a recreation of a Georgian dressing room.

The Victorian Gallery: This gallery showcases fashion from the 19th century. The exhibits include dresses, suits, and accessories from the Victorian era, as well as a recreation of a Victorian bedroom.

The Modern Gallery: This gallery showcases fashion from the 20th and 21st centuries. The exhibits include dresses, suits, and accessories from the modern era, as well as a recreation of a modern fashion studio.

The Fashion Museum has a permanent collection, but it also puts on temporary exhibitions throughout the year. These exhibitions usually concentrate on a certain designer, period, or topic.

The Fashion Museum is a great place to learn about the history of fashion. It is also a great place to get inspired by the latest fashion trends. The museum is open to the public and admission is free.

Here are some of the things you can see at the Fashion Museum Bath:

Dresses from the 17th century: These dresses are made from a variety of materials, including silk, satin, and velvet. They are decorated with lace, embroidery, and jewels.

Suits from the 18th century: These suits are made from a variety of materials, including wool, tweed, and brocade. They are decorated with buttons, braid, and piping.

Accessories from the 19th century: These accessories include hats, gloves, shoes, and jewelry. They are made from a variety of materials, including feathers, fur, and precious metals.

Dresses from the 20th century: These dresses reflect the changing fashion trends of the 20th century. They are made from a variety of materials, including cotton, linen, and polyester. They are decorated with prints, patterns, and sequins.

Suits from the 21st century: These suits reflect the latest fashion trends of the 21st century. They are made from a variety of materials, including leather, denim, and plastic. They are decorated with studs, zippers, and patches.

Here are some of the things you can do at the Fashion Museum Bath:

Take a guided tour: The Fashion Museum offers guided tours for groups of up to 20 people. Tours last for approximately one hour and cost £10 per person.

Attend a special event: The Fashion Museum hosts a variety of special events throughout the year, such as fashion shows, lectures, and workshops. These events are open to the public and tickets are usually required.

Get involved in a research project: The Fashion Museum is always looking for volunteers to help with research projects. If you are interested in fashion history, this is a great way to get involved.

Donate to the museum: The Fashion Museum relies on donations to continue its work. If you would like to support the museum, you can make a donation online or by mail.

The Fashion Museum Bath is a great place to learn about the history of fashion and to get inspired by the latest fashion trends. If you are interested in fashion, this is a must-see attraction in Bath.

5.4 The Circus

The Circus is one of Bath's most iconic landmarks, and for good reason. This stunning circular Georgian terrace is a masterpiece of architecture, and it's hard to believe that it was built over 250 years ago.

The Circus was designed by John Wood the Elder, and construction began in 1754. The terrace is made up of three tiers of classical columns, and it's crowned by a balustrade. The central garden is home to five enormous plane trees, which provide shade and create a tranquil oasis in the heart of the city.

The Circus is located in the heart of Bath, just a short walk from the Roman baths and the Royal Crescent. It's a popular spot for tourists and locals alike, and it's a great place to relax and enjoy the view.

History

The Circus was built in the mid-18th century by John Wood the Elder, a renowned architect who also designed the Royal Crescent and the Assembly Rooms in Bath. Wood was inspired by the Colosseum in Rome, and he wanted to create a similar structure in Bath that would showcase the city's Georgian architecture.

The Circus was built in three phases, with the first phase completed in 1764, the second phase completed in 1766, and the third and final phase completed in 1773. The terrace was originally intended to be a row of townhouses, but Wood changed his plans after realizing that the circular design would provide better views and more sunlight.

The Circus was an instant success, and it quickly became one of the most desirable addresses in Bath. The townhouses were rented out to wealthy merchants, aristocrats, and other members of the upper class. The Circus was also a popular spot for social gatherings, and it was often used for balls, concerts, and other events.

Architecture

The Circus is a masterpiece of Georgian architecture. The terrace is made up of three tiers of classical columns, which support a balustrade. The central garden is home to five enormous plane trees, which provide shade and create a tranquil oasis in the heart of the city.

The Circus is a perfect example of the Georgian style of architecture, which is characterized by its symmetry, proportion, and classical elements. The terrace is beautifully proportioned, and the columns and balustrade add a touch of elegance. The plane trees in the central garden provide a touch of greenery and create a sense of peace and tranquility.

The Circus Today

The Circus is still one of the most popular tourist destinations in Bath. The terrace is a popular spot for taking photographs, and it's also a great place to relax and enjoy the view. The Circus is also home to a number of shops, restaurants, and cafes, making it a great place to spend an afternoon.

If you're visiting Bath, be sure to make a stop at The Circus. It's one of the city's most iconic landmarks, and it's a great place to experience the beauty of Georgian architecture.

Things to do at The Circus

Here are a few things you can do at The Circus:

Take a walk around the terrace and admire the architecture.

Sit in the central garden and relax in the shade of the plane trees.

Visit the shops, restaurants, and cafes that line the terrace.

Take a photo of The Circus from the Royal Crescent.

Attend a concert or event at The Circus.

Getting to The Circus

The Circus is located in the heart of Bath, just a short walk from the Roman baths and the Royal Crescent. You can reach The Circus by car, bus, or train.

If you're driving, there are several car parks located near The Circus. You can also park on the street, but be aware that parking can be limited.

There are several bus stops located near The Circus. The number 1, 2, and 12 buses all stop near The Circus.

The nearest train station is Bath Spa railway station. From the station, it's a short walk to The Circus.

Tips

Here are a few tips for visiting The Circus:

Visit The Circus in the morning or evening when it's less crowded.

Wear comfortable shoes as you'll be doing a lot of walking.

Bring your camera to capture the beauty of The Circus.

Be aware that The Circus is a popular tourist destination, so expect crowds.

5.5 Sally Lunn's Historic Eating House

Sally Lunn's Historic Eating House is a hidden gem in Bath that is worth a visit for its delicious food, charming atmosphere, and fascinating history. The restaurant is located in one of Bath's oldest buildings, a 15th-century townhouse that was once home to the legendary Huguenot baker Sally Lunn.

Lunn is credited with creating the first Bath Bun, a sweet, yeasty bread that is still served at the restaurant today.

Sally Lunn's is open for breakfast, lunch, and dinner, and the menu features a variety of traditional English dishes, as well as some more modern options. The restaurant is also known for its afternoon tea, which is served in the elegant Georgian dining room.

In addition to its delicious food, Sally Lunn's is also a great place to learn about Bath's history. The restaurant has a small museum on the premises that tells the story of Sally Lunn and her famous bun. Visitors can also see the original kitchen where Lunn baked her buns, as well as some other historical artifacts.

Sally Lunn's is a popular tourist destination, but it is also a great place for locals to enjoy a meal. The restaurant is located in the heart of Bath, making it a convenient place to stop for a bite to eat before or after exploring the city.

Here is a more detailed description of Sally Lunn's Historic Eating House:

History

Sally Lunn's is one of Bath's oldest buildings, dating back to the 15th century. The house was originally built for a wealthy merchant, but it was later purchased by a Huguenot baker named Sally Lunn. Lunn was a refugee from France, and she brought her baking skills with her to England. She is credited with creating the first Bath Bun, a sweet, yeasty bread that is still served at the restaurant today.

Sally Lunn's became a popular spot for locals and visitors alike, and it continued to operate for many years. The restaurant closed in the early 20th century, but it was reopened in the 1970s by a group of local enthusiasts. The restaurant has been in continuous operation ever since.

Menu

Sally Lunn's serves a variety of traditional English dishes, as well as some more modern options. The restaurant is most famous for its Bath Buns, which are still baked to the original recipe. The buns are served warm and fresh, and they can be enjoyed plain or with butter, jam, or cream.

Other popular dishes at Sally Lunn's include the Full English Breakfast, the Roast Chicken Dinner, and the Afternoon Tea. The restaurant also has a children's menu.

Atmosphere

Sally Lunn's is located in a charming Georgian townhouse, and the restaurant has a warm and inviting atmosphere. The dining room is decorated with antiques and period furnishings, and the walls are hung with paintings and prints. The restaurant also has a small garden that is open during the summer months.

Service

The service at Sally Lunn's is friendly and attentive. The staff are knowledgeable about the menu and they are happy to make recommendations.

Sally Lunn's Historic Eating House is a hidden gem in Bath that is worth a visit. The restaurant has a delicious menu, a charming atmosphere, and friendly service. If you are looking for a unique dining experience in Bath, Sally Lunn's is the perfect place to go.

Here are some tips for visiting Sally Lunn's:

Make a reservation, especially if you are planning on dining during the peak season.

Arrive early, as the restaurant can get crowded.

Try the Bath Buns, they are the restaurant's signature dish.

Enjoy the afternoon tea in the elegant Georgian dining room.

Take a look around the museum, it tells the story of Sally Lunn and her famous bun.

Relax in the garden during the summer months.

Be sure to tip your server.

5.6 Beckford's Tower

Beckford's Tower is a folly on Lansdown Hill, just outside Bath, Somerset, England. It was built in 1827 by William Thomas Beckford, a wealthy novelist, art collector and critic. The tower is 154 feet (47 m) tall and is made of Bath stone. It is a Grade I listed building.

Beckford was inspired to build the tower after visiting the Temple of Vesta in Rome. He wanted to create a place where he could study and write in peace and quiet. The tower has a spiral staircase that leads to a viewing platform at the top. From the top of the tower, there are panoramic views of Bath and the surrounding countryside.

Beckford's Tower is a popular tourist destination. It is open to the public and can be reached by a short walk from the top of Lansdown Hill. The tower is also a popular spot for weddings and other events.

History

Beckford's Tower was built between 1826 and 1827. The architect was Henry Goodridge, a Bath architect who also designed the Royal Crescent and the Circus. The tower was built on land that Beckford had purchased in 1822.

Beckford was a wealthy man who made his fortune through his ownership of sugar plantations in Jamaica. He was also a talented artist, writer and collector. He was the author of the novel Vathek, which is considered to be one of the most important works of Gothic fiction.

Beckford lived in the tower for a few years, but he eventually moved to Italy. He died in 1844.

Architecture

Beckford's Tower is a classical folly. It is a square tower with a Doric portico. The tower is made of Bath stone and is topped with a balustrade.

The interior of the tower is divided into two floors. The ground floor is a library and study. The upper floor is a bedroom and sitting room.

Views

From the top of Beckford's Tower, there are panoramic views of Bath and the surrounding countryside. On a clear day, it is possible to see as far as Bristol and the Cotswolds.

Visiting

Beckford's Tower is open to the public from 10am to 5pm, seven days a week. Admission is £5 for adults and £3 for children.

The tower is located on Lansdown Hill, just outside Bath. It can be reached by a short walk from the top of Lansdown Hill.

Beckford's Tower is a hidden gem in Bath. It is a beautiful and historic building that offers stunning views of the city and countryside. The tower is a great place to visit for a day out or for a special event.

6. Iconic Landmarks

6.1 Bath Assembly Rooms

The Bath Assembly Rooms are a set of assembly rooms located in the heart of the World Heritage City of Bath in England. They were designed by John Wood the Younger and built between 1769 and 1771. The Assembly Rooms are a Grade I listed building and are now open to the public as a visitor attraction.

The Assembly Rooms were built to provide a place for people to meet, socialize, and enjoy entertainment. They were particularly popular during the Georgian era, when Bath was a fashionable spa town. The Assembly Rooms hosted a variety of events, including balls, concerts, dances, and card games.

The Assembly Rooms are a beautiful example of Georgian architecture. The building is made of Bath stone and features a Palladian design. The interior of the Assembly Rooms is just as impressive as the exterior. The Great Octagon is the largest room in the building and is used for concerts and dances. The Tea Room is a smaller room that is used for tea parties and other gatherings. The Card Room is used for card games and other activities.

The Bath Assembly Rooms are a popular tourist destination and are a must-see for any visitor to Bath. The Assembly Rooms offer a glimpse into the Georgian era and are a reminder of Bath's long history as a fashionable spa town.

History

The Bath Assembly Rooms were built in the late 18th century by John Wood the Younger, a renowned architect of the Georgian era. Wood was inspired by the Roman baths that he had seen in Italy, and he designed the Assembly Rooms to be a luxurious and elegant space for social gatherings.

The Assembly Rooms were completed in 1771 and were an instant success. They quickly became the center of social life in Bath, and they were used for a variety of events, including balls, concerts, and dances. The Assembly Rooms were also a popular spot for gambling, and they were said to be one of the most profitable gambling halls in England.

The Assembly Rooms continued to be popular throughout the 19th century. However, their popularity began to decline in the early 20th century, as Bath became less fashionable. The Assembly Rooms were eventually closed in 1939.

In 1952, the Bath Assembly Rooms were purchased by the National Trust, a British conservation charity. The National Trust restored the Assembly Rooms to their former glory, and they reopened to the public in 1954.

Today

Today, the Bath Assembly Rooms are a popular tourist destination. They are open to the public for tours, and they are also used for a variety of events, including concerts, dances, and weddings. The Assembly Rooms are a reminder of Bath's long history as a fashionable spa town, and they are a beautiful example of Georgian architecture.

Tours

The Bath Assembly Rooms offer a variety of tours, including guided tours, self-guided tours, and children's tours. Guided tours are led by experienced guides who can tell you about the history of the Assembly Rooms and the events that took place there. Self-guided tours allow you to explore the Assembly Rooms at your own pace. Children's tours are designed for children ages 7-12 and they include games and activities.

Events

The Bath Assembly Rooms are used for a variety of events, including concerts, dances, and weddings. Concerts are held in the Great Octagon, which is the largest room in the building. Dances are held in the Tea Room, which is a smaller room that is used for tea parties and other gatherings. Weddings are often held in the Assembly Rooms, and they can be a beautiful and memorable event.

The Bath Assembly Rooms are a beautiful and historic building that is a must-see for any visitor to Bath. The Assembly Rooms offer a glimpse into the Georgian era and are a reminder of Bath's long history as a fashionable spa town.

6.2 Bath Guildhall Market

Bath Guildhall Market is a covered market located in the heart of Bath, England. It is the oldest shopping venue in the city and has been trading for over 800 years. The market is home to a wide variety of stalls selling everything from fresh produce to handmade gifts. It is a popular tourist destination and a great place to find unique souvenirs and gifts.

The market is housed in a beautiful 19th century building that is made of Bath stone. The building has a central dome roof that provides natural light to the market. The market is open six days a week and is a great place to spend a morning or afternoon exploring.

History of Bath Guildhall Market

Bath Guildhall Market has a long and rich history. The first market on this site was established in the 12th century. The market was originally held in the open air, but it was moved indoors in the 18th century. The current market building was built in 1839.

The market has played an important role in the history of Bath. It has been a place where people have come to buy and sell goods for centuries. The market has also been a social hub where people have come to meet and exchange news.

What to See and Do at Bath Guildhall Market

Bath Guildhall Market is a great place to find unique souvenirs and gifts. The market has a wide variety of stalls selling everything from fresh produce to handmade crafts. There are also a number of cafes and restaurants in the market where you can enjoy a bite to eat.

Here are some of the things you can see and do at Bath Guildhall Market:

Visit the market's fresh produce stalls and pick up some local produce for your next meal.

Browse the market's handmade crafts stalls and find a unique souvenir or gift for your loved ones.

Enjoy a meal at one of the market's cafes or restaurants.

Take a walk around the market and soak up the atmosphere.

Tips for Visiting Bath Guildhall Market

Here are a few tips for visiting Bath Guildhall Market:

The market is open six days a week, from Monday to Saturday.

The market is busiest in the morning and early afternoon.

If you are looking for fresh produce, visit the market early in the morning.

If you are looking for handmade crafts, visit the market in the afternoon.

Be sure to bargain with the stallholders.

Enjoy a meal at one of the market's cafes or restaurants.

Bath Guildhall Market is a great place to spend a morning or afternoon exploring. The market has a wide variety of stalls selling everything from fresh produce to handmade crafts. It is a popular tourist destination and a great place to find unique souvenirs and gifts.

6.3 Bath Rugby Stadium

Bath Rugby Stadium is a rugby union stadium in Bath, England. It is the home ground of Bath Rugby, who compete in the Gallagher Premiership. The stadium has a capacity of 16,561 and is located in the heart of the city, next to the River Avon.

The stadium was built in 1899 and has undergone several renovations over the years. The most recent renovation was completed in 2014 and included the construction of a new grandstand, which increased the capacity of the stadium to 16,561.

Bath Rugby Stadium is one of the most iconic rugby stadiums in England. It has hosted many memorable matches, including the 2003 Heineken Cup Final, which Bath won against Toulouse. The stadium is also a popular venue for concerts and other events.

History

Bath Rugby Stadium was built in 1899 on the site of a former cricket ground. The stadium was originally known as the Recreation Ground and was used for both rugby and cricket. The first rugby match at the stadium was played on 20 September 1899, when Bath played Bristol. Bath won the match 10-0.

In 1905, the Recreation Ground was renamed The Rec. The Rec hosted its first international rugby match in 1907, when England played Wales. England won the match 13-3.

The Rec underwent a major renovation in 1964. The old grandstand was demolished and a new grandstand was built in its place. The new grandstand increased the capacity of the stadium to 12,000.

In 1996, The Rec hosted its first Heineken Cup match. Bath played Toulouse in the quarter-final of the competition. Bath won the match 26-19.

The Rec underwent another major renovation in 2014. The old North Stand was demolished and a new grandstand was built in its place. The new grandstand increased the capacity of the stadium to 16,561.

Facilities

Bath Rugby Stadium has a number of facilities, including:

A main grandstand with seating for 13,500 spectators

A North Stand with seating for 3,000 spectators

A South Stand with seating for 1,000 spectators

A West Stand with seating for 1,000 spectators

A 250-seat hospitality suite

A number of bars and restaurants

A club shop

A car park with capacity for 1,500 cars

Events

Bath Rugby Stadium is used for a variety of events, including:

Rugby union matches

Football matches

Concerts

Other sporting events

The Future

Bath Rugby Stadium is a popular venue for rugby union matches and other events. The stadium is well-maintained and has a number of facilities, making it a desirable venue for a variety of events.

The future of Bath Rugby Stadium is bright. The stadium is well-positioned to continue to be a popular venue for rugby union matches and other events. The stadium is also likely to undergo further renovations in the future, which will further enhance its facilities and make it an even more desirable venue.

6.4 Holburne Museum

The Holburne Museum is a fine art museum in Bath, Somerset, England. It is located in Sydney Pleasure

Gardens, a Georgian landscaped park, and is home to a collection of over 4,000 works of art, including paintings, sculptures, furniture, and decorative arts. The museum was founded in 1882 by the will of Sir William Holburne, a naval officer and art collector.

The Holburne Museum's collection is particularly strong in British art of the 18th and 19th centuries. The museum has paintings by Gainsborough, Reynolds, and Romney, as well as sculptures by Canova and Flaxman. The museum also has a significant collection of furniture, porcelain, and silver.

The Holburne Museum is housed in a Grade I listed building that was designed by Charles Harcourt Masters. The building was originally built as a private residence in the early 18th century. It was acquired by the Holburne family in 1765, and it was later used as a museum by Sir William Holburne. The museum underwent a major renovation in the early 2000s, and it reopened in 2006.

The Holburne Museum is a popular tourist destination in Bath. It is open to the public from Tuesday to Sunday, and admission is free for children under 18 and for members. The museum offers a variety of educational programs and events, including exhibitions, workshops, and lectures.

The Collection

The Holburne Museum's collection is divided into three main areas: fine art, decorative arts, and silver.

The fine art collection includes paintings, sculptures, and drawings. The paintings date from the 16th to the 19th centuries, and they include works by

British, Italian, and French artists. The sculptures in the collection date from the 17th to the 19th centuries, and they include works by Italian, French, and British sculptors. The drawings in the collection date from the 16th to the 19th centuries, and they include works by British, Italian, and French artists.

The decorative arts collection includes furniture, porcelain, silver, and glass. The furniture in the collection dates from the 17th to the 19th centuries, and it includes pieces from England, France, and Italy. The porcelain in the collection dates from the 17th to the 19th centuries, and it includes pieces from China, Japan, and Europe. The silver in the collection dates from the 17th to the 19th centuries, and it includes pieces from England, France, and Italy. The glass in the collection dates from the 17th to the 19th centuries, and it includes pieces from England, France, and Italy.

The Building

The Holburne Museum is housed in a Grade I listed building that was designed by Charles Harcourt Masters. The building was originally built as a private residence in the early 18th century. It was acquired by the Holburne family in 1765, and it was later used as a museum by Sir William Holburne. The museum underwent a major renovation in the early 2000s, and it reopened in 2006.

The building is a three-story Georgian townhouse. It has a symmetrical facade with a central portico. The interior of the building is decorated in a variety of styles, including Georgian, Regency, and Victorian. The museum's galleries are located on the ground and first floors. The second floor is home to the museum's library, study, and conservation department.

The Museum Today

The Holburne Museum is a popular tourist destination in Bath. It is open to the public from Tuesday to Sunday, and admission is free for children under 18 and for members. The museum offers a variety of educational programs and events, including exhibitions, workshops, and lectures.

The Holburne Museum is a valuable resource for the people of Bath and for the wider community. It is a place where people can learn about art and history, and it is a place where people can come to be inspired.

6.5 Bath Postal Museum

The Bath Postal Museum is a fascinating place to learn about the history of mail delivery in Britain.

The museum is located in a beautiful Georgian building in the heart of Bath, and it is home to a wide variety of exhibits, including:

A history of the Royal Mail, from its humble beginnings in the 17th century to its modern-day incarnation as a global network.

A collection of historical mail coaches, which were used to deliver mail before the advent of the railways.

A display of early postal stamps, including the famous Penny Black, the first adhesive postage stamp in the world.

A recreation of a Victorian post office, where visitors can learn about the daily routines of postal workers in the 19th century.

The Bath Postal Museum is a great place to learn about the history of mail delivery and the role that the Royal Mail has played in British society. It is also a fun and interactive place to visit, with plenty of hands-on exhibits for children and adults alike.

History of the Bath Postal Museum

The Bath Postal Museum was founded in 1979 by Audrey and Harold Swindells, a local couple who were passionate about the history of the Royal Mail. The museum was originally located in the basement of the Swindells' home, but it moved to its current location in 1985.

The museum has been growing ever since, and it now has a collection of over 10,000 objects related to the history of the Royal Mail. The museum also has a team of dedicated volunteers who work to ensure that the museum is a welcoming and informative place for visitors of all ages.

Exhibits

The Bath Postal Museum has a wide variety of exhibits that tell the story of the Royal Mail. Some of the highlights include:

A history of the Royal Mail, from its humble beginnings in the 17th century to its modern-day incarnation as a global network.

A collection of historical mail coaches, which were used to deliver mail before the advent of the railways.

A display of early postal stamps, including the famous Penny Black, the first adhesive postage stamp in the world.

A recreation of a Victorian post office, where visitors can learn about the daily routines of postal workers in the 19th century.

Activities

In addition to its exhibits, the Bath Postal Museum also offers a variety of activities for visitors of all ages. Some of the activities include:

Postbox hunt - Children can search for postboxes around Bath and learn about the history of postboxes.

Stamp making - Children can make their own stamps using traditional methods.

Postman's round - Visitors can take a guided tour of the museum and learn about the daily routines of a postman.

Location and Contact Information

The Bath Postal Museum is located at 16 Broad Street, Bath, Somerset, BA1 2AW. The museum is open from 10am to 4pm, Tuesday to Sunday. Admission is £6 for adults, £4 for children, and free for children under 5.

6.6 Theatre Royal Bath

The Theatre Royal Bath is a Grade II listed theatre in Bath, England. It was built in 1805 and is one of the most important surviving examples of Georgian theatre architecture. The theatre has a capacity for an audience of around 900 and has hosted a wide range of performances over the years, including plays, musicals, operas, and ballets.

The Theatre Royal Bath was designed by John Palmer, George Dance the Younger, and C. J. Phipps. The building is in the Georgian style and features a portico with four Corinthian columns. The interior of the theatre is decorated with a lavish ceiling and chandeliers.

The Theatre Royal Bath was opened on 25 September 1805 with a performance of John Home's play Douglas. The theatre quickly became a popular venue for both local and national performers. In the early 19th century, the theatre was home to the Bath Philharmonic Society, which gave regular concerts.

In the 1850s, the Theatre Royal Bath underwent a major renovation. The auditorium was enlarged and the stage was rebuilt. The theatre also received a new roof and a new entrance.

The Theatre Royal Bath continued to be a popular venue for performances throughout the 20th century. In the 1960s, the theatre was home to the Bath

Festival, which featured a variety of performances, including plays, musicals, and opera.

In the 1990s, the Theatre Royal Bath underwent another major renovation. The auditorium was restored to its original Georgian design and the stage was modernized. The theatre also received a new lighting system and a new sound system.

Today, the Theatre Royal Bath is one of the most popular theatres in the UK. It hosts a wide range of performances, including plays, musicals, operas, and ballets. The theatre is also home to the Bath Festival, which takes place every year in July.

The Theatre Royal Bath is a Grade II listed building, which means that it is considered to be of special architectural or historic interest. The theatre is a popular tourist destination and is a significant part of Bath's cultural heritage.

Here are some of the most notable performances that have taken place at the Theatre Royal Bath:

The premiere of John Home's play Douglas in 1805

The Bath Philharmonic Society's concerts in the early 19th century

The Bath Festival in the 1960s

The restoration of the theatre in the 1990s

The current range of performances, including plays, musicals, operas, and ballets

The Theatre Royal Bath is a significant part of Bath's cultural heritage and is a popular tourist destination.

7. Authentic Experiences in Bath

7.1 Bath Farmers Market

Bath is also home to a thriving farmers market, which is the perfect place to experience the city's authentic charm.

The Bath Farmers Market is held every Saturday from 9am to 12pm, May through October. It's located in the heart of the city, on the waterfront. The market is a great place to find fresh, local produce, meats, cheeses, and other food items. You can also find handcrafted goods, such as jewelry, pottery, and woodwork.

The Bath Farmers Market is a great place to meet locals and learn about the city's agricultural community. It's also a great place to find unique gifts and souvenirs. If you're looking for an authentic experience in Bath, be sure to visit the farmers market.

Here are some of the things you can do at the Bath Farmers Market:

Shop for fresh, local produce: The Bath Farmers Market is a great place to find fresh, seasonal produce. You can find everything from fruits and vegetables to herbs and flowers.

Buy local meats and cheeses: The Bath Farmers Market also has a wide selection of local meats and cheeses. You can find everything from beef and pork to lamb and goat cheese.

Sample handcrafted goods: In addition to food, the Bath Farmers Market also has a variety of handcrafted goods for sale. You can find jewelry, pottery, woodwork, and more.

Meet the locals: The Bath Farmers Market is a great place to meet locals and learn about the city's agricultural community. The vendors are always happy to chat about their products and share their stories.

Enjoy the atmosphere: The Bath Farmers Market is a vibrant and lively place. It's a great place to spend a Saturday morning, people-watching and enjoying the fresh air.

If you're looking for an authentic experience in Bath, be sure to visit the farmers market. It's a great place to find fresh, local food, handcrafted goods, and friendly people.

Here are some additional tips for visiting the Bath Farmers Market:

Arrive early: The market can get crowded, so it's best to arrive early.

Bring a reusable bag: The market encourages shoppers to bring their own reusable bags.

Be prepared to bargain: Some vendors are willing to bargain, so don't be afraid to ask.

Take your time: There's no need to rush. Take your time and enjoy the atmosphere.

I hope you enjoy your visit to the Bath Farmers Market!

7.2 Bath Breweries and Distilleries

Bath is a city with a rich history and culture, and its brewing and distilling traditions are no exception. From small, independent breweries to large-scale distilleries, Bath is home to a thriving drinks industry.

Breweries

Bath has a long history of brewing, dating back to the 17th century. The city's first brewery, the Abbey Ales Brewery, was founded in 1675. Today, Bath is home to a number of independent breweries, including Bath Ales, Electric Bear Brewing Co., and The Bath Brew House.

Bath Ales is one of the largest independent breweries in the UK. The brewery was founded in

1995 and now produces a wide range of award-winning ales, including its flagship beer, Batham's Bitter.

Electric Bear Brewing Co. is a small, independent brewery that was founded in 2012. The brewery specializes in producing hoppy, aromatic beers.

The Bath Brew House is a brewpub that was founded in 2010. The pub has its own on-site brewery, which produces a range of beers that are available to drink in the pub or to take away.

Distilleries

Bath is also home to a number of distilleries, including Bath Gin and Bath Botanics.

Bath Gin is a small-batch gin distillery that was founded in 2013. The distillery uses a variety of botanicals to create its gin, including juniper berries, coriander, and angelica root.

Bath Botanics is a distillery that specializes in producing organic spirits. The distillery uses a variety of herbs and flowers to create its spirits, including lavender, chamomile, and rosehip.

Authentic Experiences

There are a number of ways to experience Bath's brewing and distilling traditions. Here are a few suggestions:

Take a brewery tour: Bath Ales offers tours of its brewery, which give visitors a behind-the-scenes look at the brewing process.

Visit a distillery: Bath Gin offers tours of its distillery, which give visitors a chance to learn about the gin-making process and sample the distillery's products.

Attend a beer festival: Bath hosts a number of beer festivals throughout the year, including the Bath Beer Festival and the Bath Ales Spring Beer Festival.

Visit a pub: Bath has a number of pubs that serve locally-brewed beer. Some of the city's most popular pubs include The White Hart, The Bear, and The Swan.

Bath's brewing and distilling traditions are a part of the city's rich history and culture. Whether you're a beer lover or a gin enthusiast, there are a number of ways to experience these traditions during your visit to Bath.

7.3 Bath's Culinary Delights

Bath is a city with a rich culinary history, dating back to Roman times. Today, the city is home to a diverse range of restaurants, cafes, and bars, serving up everything from traditional British fare to international cuisine. Whether you're looking for a casual lunch or a fine dining experience, you're sure to find something to your taste in Bath.

Here are a few of the best places to experience Bath's culinary delights:

The Pump Room: This iconic restaurant is located in the heart of Bath, and it's the perfect place to enjoy a traditional English meal. The menu features dishes like roast beef with Yorkshire pudding, fish and chips, and sticky toffee pudding.

Bath Priory: This Michelin-starred restaurant offers a modern take on British cuisine. The tasting menu changes seasonally, but you can expect to find dishes like seared scallops with cauliflower puree, and roasted lamb with mint sauce.

The Olive Tree: This Mediterranean restaurant is a popular spot for both locals and visitors. The menu features a wide variety of dishes, including pasta, pizza, and seafood.

The Circus: This trendy bar and restaurant is located in a beautiful Georgian building. The menu features modern British cuisine, and the bar has a wide selection of cocktails and beers.

The Pig and Whistle: This traditional English pub is a great place to enjoy a pint of beer and a hearty meal. The menu features pub classics like fish and chips, bangers and mash, and shepherd's pie.

In addition to its many restaurants, Bath is also home to a number of markets where you can buy fresh produce, meats, cheeses, and other local delicacies. The Bath Farmers' Market is held every Saturday morning, and the Bath Christmas Market is held every December.

If you're looking for a unique culinary experience, you can also take a cooking class in Bath. There are a number of different schools and companies that offer cooking classes, from beginner to advanced levels.

Bath is a city with a lot to offer foodies of all ages. With its wide variety of restaurants, markets, and cooking classes, you're sure to find something to your taste in this historic city.

7.4 Guided Walking Tours

There are many ways to experience Bath, but one of the best ways is to take a guided walking tour.

There are many different guided walking tours available in Bath, each of which offers a unique perspective on the city. Some tours focus on the Roman history of Bath, while others explore the Georgian architecture. There are also tours that focus on the city's literary history, or its food and drink scene.

No matter what your interests are, there is sure to be a guided walking tour in Bath that is perfect for you. Here are a few of the most popular guided walking tours in Bath:

Roman Baths Tour: This tour takes you to the Roman baths, which are one of the most popular tourist attractions in Bath. You will learn about the history of the baths and how they were used by the Romans.

Georgian Bath Tour: This tour takes you through the Georgian city of Bath, which is a UNESCO World Heritage Site. You will see some of the most beautiful Georgian architecture in the world, including the Royal Crescent and the Circus.

Literary Bath Tour: This tour takes you to some of the places in Bath that were associated with famous writers, such as Jane Austen and William Wordsworth. You will also learn about the city's literary history.

Food and Drink Tour: This tour takes you to some of the best restaurants and pubs in Bath. You will learn about the city's food and drink culture, and you will get to sample some of the local delicacies.

In addition to these popular tours, there are many other guided walking tours available in Bath. You can find a full list of tours on the Visit Bath website.

Guided walking tours are a great way to learn about Bath and to see the city from a different perspective. They are also a great way to meet other people who are interested in Bath. If you are planning a visit to Bath, I highly recommend taking a guided walking tour.

Additional Information

Cost: Guided walking tours in Bath typically cost between £10 and £20 per person.

Duration: Guided walking tours in Bath typically last for 1-2 hours.

Meeting point: Guided walking tours in Bath typically meet at the Roman Baths or at other central locations.

Booking: Guided walking tours in Bath can be booked online or in person at the Visit Bath visitor center.

Tips

Book your tour in advance: Guided walking tours in Bath can sell out, so it is a good idea to book your tour in advance.

Dress comfortably: You will be doing a lot of walking, so make sure to wear comfortable shoes.

Bring water and sunscreen: It can get hot in Bath, so be sure to bring water and sunscreen.

Have fun! Guided walking tours are a great way to learn about Bath and to see the city from a different perspective.

7.5 Exploring Bath's Parks and Gardens

Royal Victoria Park: This park is one of the largest in Bath, and it is a great place to relax and enjoy the outdoors. There are plenty of things to do in the park, including walking, cycling, boating, and playing sports. The park is also home to a number of attractions, such as the Royal Victoria Baths, the Holburne Museum, and the Alexandra Park Pavilion.

Pulteney Gardens: These beautiful gardens are located in the heart of Bath, and they are a popular spot for locals and tourists alike. The gardens are home to a variety of flowers, plants, and trees, and they are a great place to take a stroll, have a picnic, or simply relax and enjoy the scenery.

The Parade Gardens: These gardens are located on the banks of the River Avon, and they offer stunning views of the city. The gardens are a great place to take a walk, have a picnic, or simply relax and enjoy the atmosphere.

Sydney Gardens: These gardens are located on the outskirts of Bath, and they are a great place to escape the hustle and bustle of the city. The gardens are home to a variety of flowers, plants, and trees, and they are a great place to take a walk, have a picnic, or simply relax and enjoy the peace and quiet.

Bath Botanical Gardens: These gardens are home to a wide variety of plants from all over the world. The gardens are a great place to learn about plants, and they are also a great place to take a walk, have a picnic, or simply relax and enjoy the scenery.

7.6 Bath Festivals and Events

Bath is a city that is full of life and culture, and there are always a variety of festivals and events happening throughout the year. Whether you're interested in music, theater, food, or art, you're sure to find something to enjoy.

Here are a few of the most popular festivals and events in Bath:

Bath International Music Festival: This festival takes place every October and features a wide range of classical music performances from around the world.

Bath Literature Festival: This festival takes place every November and features a variety of talks, readings, and workshops from authors and literary figures.

Bath Film Festival: This festival takes place every February and features a selection of independent and foreign films.

Bath Comedy Festival: This festival takes place every May and features a variety of stand-up comedy performances from up-and-coming and established comedians.

Bath Fringe Festival: This festival takes place every July and features a wide range of performances, from theater and dance to music and comedy.

Bath Christmas Market: This market takes place every December and features over 100 stalls selling festive food, drink, and gifts.

In addition to these major festivals, there are also a number of smaller events happening throughout the year. For example, the city hosts a number of concerts and plays in its theaters and concert halls. There are also a number of art exhibitions and open studios, as well as a variety of food and drink festivals.

No matter what your interests are, you're sure to find something to enjoy in Bath. With its rich history and vibrant culture, the city is a great place to experience a variety of authentic experiences.

Bath is a city with a lot to offer, and there are endless possibilities for authentic experiences. With its rich history, vibrant culture, and stunning scenery, Bath is a city that is sure to leave a lasting impression.

8. Recommended Day Itineraries

8.1 One Day in Bath: Highlights Tour

Morning: Arrive in Bath and check into your hotel. In the morning, visit the Roman Baths, one of the most popular tourist attractions in Bath. The baths are a UNESCO World Heritage Site and date back to the Roman occupation of Britain. You can take a tour of the baths, learn about the history of the site, and see the Sacred Spring, the Roman Temple, and the Roman Bath House.

Afternoon: After visiting the Roman Baths, take a stroll through the city center. Bath is a beautiful Georgian city with many historic buildings, including the Royal Crescent, the Circus, and the

Assembly Rooms. You can also visit the Jane Austen Centre, which is dedicated to the life and work of the famous author.

Evening: In the evening, enjoy a traditional English dinner at one of Bath's many restaurants. After dinner, take a walk along the River Avon or visit one of the city's many pubs.

Here are some other things you can do in Bath if you have more time:

Visit the Holburne Museum, which houses a collection of art and antiquities.

Take a boat trip on the River Avon.

Go shopping in Bath's many boutiques and department stores.

Visit the Bath Christmas Market, which is held from late November to December.

8.2 Two Days in Bath: Immersive Experience

Day 1

Start your day with a visit to the Roman Baths, one of the best-preserved Roman baths in the world. You can take a guided tour of the baths, or simply wander around and explore on your own.

After visiting the Roman Baths, take a stroll through the city's beautiful Georgian architecture. Be sure to check out the Royal Crescent, a row of 30 terraced houses that is considered one of the finest examples of Georgian architecture in the world.

In the afternoon, take a ride on the Bath Skyline Gondola. The gondola offers stunning views of the city and the surrounding countryside.

For dinner, try one of Bath's many restaurants. Be sure to try some of the local cuisine, such as Bath chicken or Bath chap.

After dinner, take a walk along the River Avon. The river is a great place to relax and enjoy the evening atmosphere.

Day 2

On your second day in Bath, you can visit some of the city's other attractions, such as the Bath Abbey, the Jane Austen Centre, or the Holburne Museum.

You can also take a day trip to one of the many nearby towns or villages, such as Wells, Salisbury, or Stonehenge.

This is just one possible itinerary for a two-day immersive experience in Bath. There are many other things to see and do in this beautiful city, so you can tailor your itinerary to your own interests.

8.3 Three Days in Bath: History and Relaxation

Day 1: Explore the city's history

Morning: Start your day with a visit to the Roman Baths, one of the most popular tourist attractions in Bath. See the original Roman baths, learn about the history of the site, and take a dip in the thermal waters.

Afternoon: After the Roman Baths, head to Bath Abbey, a beautiful Gothic cathedral that is one of the most important religious buildings in the UK. Take a tour of the abbey, climb to the top of the tower for stunning views of the city, and enjoy a peaceful moment of reflection in the cathedral's tranquil surroundings.

Evening: In the evening, enjoy a traditional English meal at one of Bath's many restaurants. Try the local speciality, Bath chicken, or sample some of the city's famous clotted cream.

Day 2: Relax and enjoy the spa town

Morning: On your second day in Bath, take some time to relax and enjoy the city's spa facilities. Thermae Bath Spa is a popular choice, with its rooftop pool offering stunning views of the city.

Afternoon: After a morning of relaxation, head out to explore some of Bath's other attractions. The Holburne Museum is a great place to see a collection of art and antiquities, and the Jane Austen Centre is a must-visit for fans of the famous author.

Evening: In the evening, enjoy a leisurely stroll along the city's famous Royal Crescent, a row of elegant Georgian townhouses.

Day 3: Explore the surrounding countryside

Morning: On your third and final day in Bath, take a day trip to explore the surrounding countryside. The Cotswolds are a beautiful area of rolling hills and villages, and are well worth a visit.

Afternoon: After exploring the Cotswolds, return to Bath for a final evening in the city. Enjoy a farewell meal at one of Bath's many restaurants, and take some time to reflect on your trip.

8.4 Four Days in Bath: Cultural Delights

Day 1: Explore the city center

Visit the Roman Baths

Stroll through the city center

Stop by the Pulteney Bridge

Head to the Pump Room for a cream tea

Take in a performance at the Theatre Royal

Day 2: Visit the surrounding countryside

Take a trip to the village of Cheddar

Visit the Cheddar Gorge

Visit the village of Lacock

Go hiking or biking in the surrounding countryside

Day 3: Explore the Jane Austen Festival

Attend concerts, plays, and exhibitions

Day 4: Relax and enjoy the spa town

Visit one of the many spas in Bath

Stroll through the Royal Crescent

Enjoy a farewell dinner at one of Bath's many restaurants.

8.5 Five Days in Bath: Exploring Beyond the City

Day 1: Bath

Visit the Roman Baths, one of the most popular tourist attractions in Bath. The baths were built in the first century AD and are still in use today.

After your visit to the baths, take a walk around the city center. Be sure to stop by the Pulteney Bridge, a beautiful Georgian bridge that spans the River Avon.

In the afternoon, visit the Jane Austen Centre, a museum dedicated to the life and work of the famous author.

In the evening, enjoy a traditional English meal at one of Bath's many restaurants.

Day 2: The Cotswolds

On your second day, you can explore the Cotswolds, a beautiful area of countryside located north of Bath.

The Cotswolds are known for their rolling hills, pretty villages, and honey-colored stone cottages.

There are many things to see and do in the Cotswolds, including visiting historic towns and villages, exploring the countryside on foot or by bike, and sampling the local produce.

Some of the most popular villages in the Cotswolds include Bourton-on-the-Water, Bibury, and Cirencester.

Day 3: Stonehenge

On your third day, you can visit Stonehenge, a mysterious prehistoric monument located about 100 miles west of Bath.

Stonehenge is thought to have been built around 3000 BC and is one of the most famous archaeological sites in the world.

There are many theories about the purpose of Stonehenge, but its true meaning remains a mystery.

You can visit Stonehenge as part of a guided tour or explore it on your own.

Day 4: Bristol

On your fourth day, you can visit Bristol, a vibrant city located about 20 miles south of Bath.

Bristol is known for its history, culture, and its role in the transatlantic slave trade.

The city is home to a number of museums and art galleries, as well as a thriving music scene.

Some of the most popular attractions in Bristol include the Bristol Museum and Art Gallery, the Clifton Suspension Bridge, and the SS Great Britain.

Day 5: Bath

On your last day, you can relax and enjoy your last few hours in Bath.

Be sure to take a walk around the city center and visit some of your favorite places one last time.

You can also do some last-minute shopping or enjoy a farewell meal at one of Bath's many restaurants.

9. Practical Information

9.1 Public Transportation in Bath

It is easy to get around without a car. The city has a good public transportation system, which includes buses, trains, and taxis.

Buses

Buses are the most common way to get around Bath. The bus network is extensive and covers all parts of the city. Buses are also relatively inexpensive, with a single fare costing £2.20.

Trains

Trains are another good option for getting around Bath. The Bath Spa railway station is located in the city center and is served by trains from London, Bristol, and other major cities. Train tickets are generally more expensive than bus tickets, but they can be a good option if you are traveling long distances.

Taxis

Taxis are a convenient way to get around Bath, but they can be expensive. Taxis are metered, and fares start at £3.20.

Bicycles

Bicycles are a great way to get around Bath. The city has a number of bike lanes and paths, and it is relatively flat, making it easy to ride a bike. You can rent bicycles from a number of shops in the city center.

Passes and Tickets

There are a number of passes and tickets available that can save you money on public transportation in Bath. The Bath Bus Pass is a one-day pass that allows you unlimited travel on buses in Bath. The pass costs £5.50 for adults and £4.00 for children. The Bath Railcard is a discount card for train travel in the UK. The card costs £30 for a year and gives you a third off the price of train tickets.

Tips for Using Public Transportation in Bath

Buy a bus pass or train ticket to save money.

Use the Bath Bus app to track buses and plan your journey.

Check the train times before you travel.

Be aware of the taxi fares and book a taxi in advance if you are traveling during peak times.

Bring a bicycle with you if you are planning on doing a lot of walking.

Bath is a great city to explore by public transportation. The city has a good network of buses, trains, and taxis, and it is easy to get around without a car. With a little planning, you can easily get to all of the city's attractions without breaking the bank.

9.2 Money-Saving Tips

Bath is a beautiful city with a lot to offer visitors, but it can also be expensive. Here are some tips on how to save money while you're in Bath:

Book your accommodation in advance. The best way to get a good deal on accommodation is to book in advance. You can often find discounts if you book online or if you book for multiple nights.

Avoid the tourist traps. There are a lot of tourist traps in Bath that charge high prices for mediocre food and experiences. Do some research before you go and find the hidden gems that offer great value for money.

Take advantage of free activities. There are a lot of free things to do in Bath, such as visiting the Roman Baths, walking around the city center, or taking a boat ride on the River Avon.

Cook your own meals. Eating out in Bath can be expensive. If you're on a tight budget, it's much cheaper to cook your own meals. There are a number of supermarkets in Bath where you can buy groceries.

Take advantage of student discounts. If you're a student, you may be able to get discounts on admission to attractions, travel, and accommodation.

Use public transportation. Bath is a small city and it's easy to get around by public transportation. You can save money by buying a day pass or by using the bus or train system.

Walk or bike. Bath is a very walkable city and it's a great way to see the sights and get some exercise. If you're feeling adventurous, you can also rent a bike.

Be flexible with your plans. If you're willing to be flexible with your plans, you can often find last-minute deals on attractions, accommodation, and activities.

By following these tips, you can save money and still have a great time in Bath.

Here are some additional tips for saving money in Bath:

Visit during the off-season. Bath is busiest during the summer months, so if you can, try to visit during the shoulder seasons (spring or fall) or during the winter. You'll find lower prices on accommodation, attractions, and activities.

Consider staying in a hostel or guesthouse. Hostels and guesthouses are a great way to save money on accommodation. You can often find shared dormitories for as little as £10 per night.

Pack your own snacks and drinks. Eating out in Bath can be expensive, so it's a good idea to pack your own snacks and drinks. You can save money by bringing your own breakfast, lunch, and snacks.

Take advantage of free walking tours. There are a number of free walking tours in Bath that are a great way to learn about the city's history and architecture.

Join a local club or group. There are a number of local clubs and groups in Bath that offer discounts on activities and events. Joining a club or group is a great way to meet new people and save money.

9.3 Bath's Shopping Scene

Bath is a great place to shop, with a wide variety of stores to choose from. Whether you're looking for high-end fashion, unique souvenirs, or just a few everyday items, you're sure to find it in Bath.

Here are a few of the best places to shop in Bath:

The High Street

The Royal Crescent

Pierpont Arcade

Bath Market

Independent shops in the city center

Here are a few ideas for what to buy in Bath:

Bath-themed souvenirs, such as tea towels, mugs, and magnets

Bath-made products, such as honey, fudge, and toiletries

Fashion and accessories from high-end stores

Unique items from independent shops

The best time to shop in Bath is during the week, when the city is less crowded. However, if you're looking for a more lively atmosphere, you may want to shop on the weekend.

Here are a few tips for shopping in Bath:

Be sure to bargain at the market.

Ask for discounts at independent shops.

Take advantage of free shipping offers when shopping online.

Compare prices before you buy.

Don't forget to haggle!

Bath is a great place to shop, and with so much to choose from, you're sure to find something special to take home. So what are you waiting for? Start shopping today!

9.4 Healthcare and Emergency Services

Bath is a well-served city when it comes to healthcare. There are a number of hospitals, GP surgeries, and other healthcare providers in the city, as well as a range of emergency services.

Hospitals

The main hospital in Bath is the Royal United Hospitals Bath (RUH). The RUH is a large teaching hospital with a wide range of services, including accident and emergency, inpatient wards, outpatient clinics, and a maternity unit. The RUH is located on Combe Park in the south of Bath.

There are also a number of smaller hospitals in Bath, including:

The Royal National Hospital for Rheumatic Diseases

The Royal National Hospital for Orthopaedics and Burns

The Bath Community Hospital

GP Surgeries

There are over 50 GP surgeries in Bath. GP surgeries provide primary care services, such as routine appointments, vaccinations, and referrals to other healthcare providers.

To find a GP surgery in Bath, you can use the NHS website or contact your local council.

Other Healthcare Providers

In addition to hospitals and GP surgeries, there are a number of other healthcare providers in Bath, including:

Dentists

Opticians

Pharmacies

Physiotherapists

Occupational therapists

Speech and language therapists

Emergency Services

If you have a medical emergency, you should call 999. 999 is the emergency number for the police, fire brigade, and ambulance service.

If your emergency is not life-threatening, you can call NHS 111. NHS 111 is a free telephone number that you can call for advice on healthcare matters.

Other Information

The NHS website has more information about healthcare in Bath. You can also contact the Bath and North East Somerset Council for more information.

Here are some additional tips for staying healthy in Bath:

 Get vaccinated against common diseases, such as flu and meningitis.

 See your GP for regular check-ups.

 Eat a healthy diet.

Exercise regularly.

Get enough sleep.

Manage stress.

Avoid smoking and excessive alcohol consumption.

By following these tips, you can help to stay healthy while you are in Bath.

10. Conclusion

As we reach the end of our journey through the enchanting city of Bath, let us take a moment to recap the highlights and reflect on the memories we have made. Bath is a city steeped in history, beauty, and cultural significance, offering a truly immersive experience for every traveler.

10.1 Recap of Bath's Highlights

Throughout this guide, we have explored the best attractions, hidden gems, and authentic experiences that Bath has to offer. From the ancient Roman Baths that transport us back in time to the iconic Georgian architecture that graces the streets, each highlight has added to the tapestry of Bath's allure. We have wandered through the stunning Royal

Crescent, marveled at the intricate beauty of Bath Abbey, and indulged in the local flavors and culinary delights that make this city a gastronomic paradise. We have also ventured beyond the city limits to discover rural retreats and embraced the tranquility of the surrounding countryside.

10.2 Final Thoughts

As we conclude our journey, we hope that this guide has ignited your passion for Bath and provided you with the knowledge and inspiration to make the most of your visit. Bath is a city that captivates the senses, immerses you in its rich history, and leaves an indelible mark on your soul. It is a place where time seems to stand still, allowing you to truly savor the moments and create lasting memories.

As you explore Bath's cobblestone streets, indulge in its culinary delights, and immerse yourself in its cultural treasures, remember to take the time to slow down and embrace the city's unique ambiance. Let yourself be enchanted by the beauty of the architecture, the warmth of the locals, and the rich tapestry of stories that lie within every corner.

Whether you have spent a day or a week in Bath, it is our sincerest hope that this guide has helped you discover the city's hidden gems, create unforgettable itineraries, and delve into the authentic experiences that make Bath a destination like no other.

As you bid farewell to this extraordinary city, take a piece of Bath with you. Let the memories linger, and may they inspire you to seek out new adventures and embrace the beauty and history that await in other corners of the world.

Thank you for joining us on this remarkable journey through Bath. May your travels be filled with wonder, discovery, and the joy of experiencing the world's treasures. Safe travels, and may your next adventure be as captivating as your time in Bath.

Printed in Great Britain
by Amazon

25839520R00106